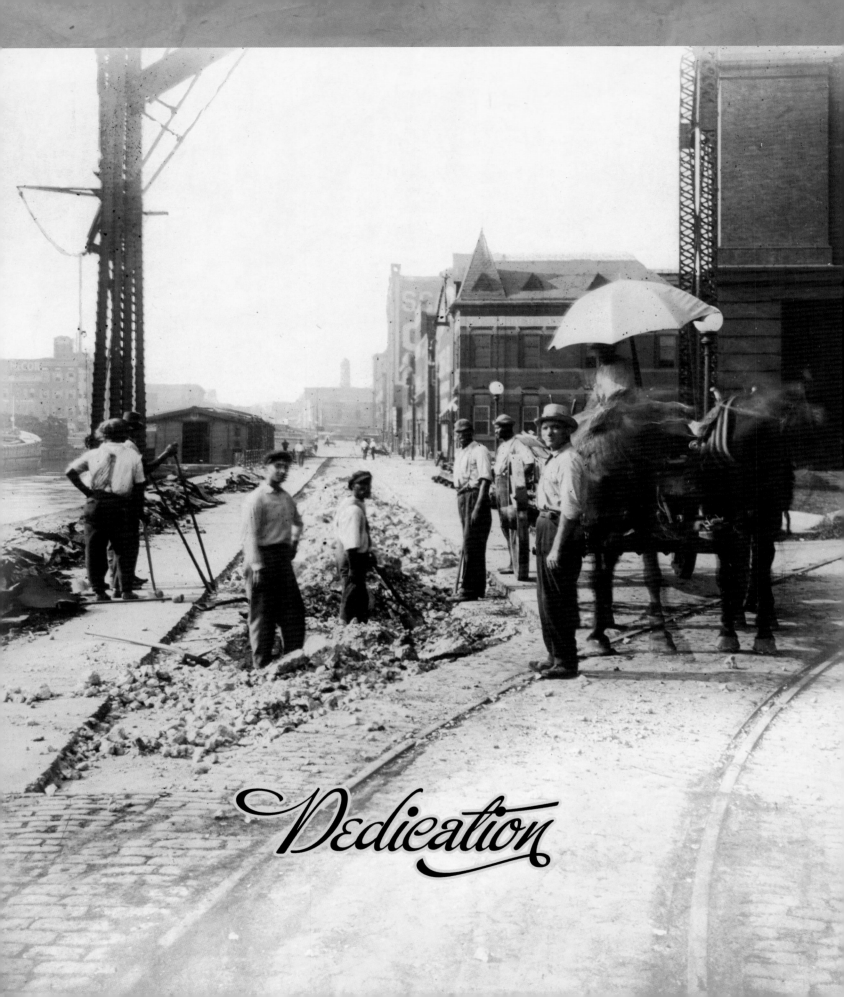

Dedication

Maryland's highway system is a vital contributor to the productivity and competitiveness of our state, as well as critical to our prosperity and quality of life.

Traveled by millions of us in Maryland every day, our highway network exists as the result of the hard work and dedication of the hundreds of thousands who have worked for the State Roads Commission, the State Highway Administration, the Maryland Transportation Authority and our private industry partners during the past 100 years.

I am honored to recognize the leadership and innovative spirit of those who have worked to improve the science of highway planning, engineering, construction, maintenance and operations. This book gives Marylanders the chance to see the excellence that these individuals have repeatedly demonstrated in delivering products and services to our people, often without the public recognition they deserve.

This book is dedicated to the men and women who have planned, designed, built, operated and maintained the roads and bridges on which we depend every single day. On behalf of the citizens of Maryland, thank you.

Martin O'Malley
Governor

As we celebrate the 100th Anniversary of the State Roads Commission (SRC), it is an appropriate time for us to reflect on the accomplishments of the industry during the past century. The SRC was the precursor to the State Highway Administration, Motor Vehicle Administration and the Maryland Transportation Authority, building the first paved roads in Maryland, and some of the first in the nation. This anniversary allows us to examine not only how modern roads and highways helped to shape the 20th and 21st centuries in Maryland, but to consider how we will meet tomorrow's challenges as well.

Looking to the future, we face challenges that include a fundamentally changing global economy, greater uncertainty regarding energy supplies and prices, increasing environmental concerns, congestion, aging pavements and bridges, costs rising faster than available revenues, rising customer expectations and a demand for greater accountability in government.

The Maryland Department of Transportation is fortunate to have two superb highway agencies – the State Highway Administration and the Maryland Transportation Authority. We are also privileged to work with innovative civil engineering design firms, safe and efficient contractors, and committed small businesses and disadvantaged enterprises. It is through their efforts that Maryland continues to be recognized as a national leader in highway transportation.

I am confident that our collective experience in overcoming great challenges over the past 100 years will be invaluable in helping to make our approach to the next 100 years more customer driven than ever.

John D. Porcari
Secretary
Maryland Department of Transportation

Executive Committee Members

Governor
Harry R. Hughes
*Honorary Chairman
& Transportation
Secretary (1971-1977)*

Bill K. Hellmann
*Transportation
Secretary (1984-1987)*

Ronald L. Freeland
*Maryland
Transportation
Authority
Executive Secretary*

John D. Porcari
*Transportation
Secretary and
Centennial Chairman*

O. James Lighthizer
*Transportation
Secretary (1991-1994)*

John Kuo
*Motor Vehicle
Administrator*

Anne Ferro
*President & CEO,
Maryland Motor
Truck Association*

David Winstead
*Transportation
Secretary (1995-1998)*

Neil J. Pedersen
*State Highway
Administrator*

Donald C. Fry
*President, Greater
Baltimore Committee*

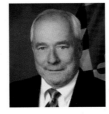
David W. Edgerley
*Secretary, Department
of Business & Economic
Development*

James J. White
*Maryland Port
Administration
Executive Director*

Nelson Castellanos
*Federal Highway
Division Administrator*

Walter E.
Woodford, Jr., P.E.
*Commissioner,
Maryland
Transportation
Authority*

Paul Wiedefeld
*Maryland Transit
Administrator*

Timothy Maloney
*Maryland General
Assembly (1979-1995)*

Timothy Campbell
*Executive Director,
Maryland Aviation
Administration*

A century of modern road building.

Mar**100**nial
years
1908 • 2008

Moving *Maryland* forward.

Harold J. Counihan

Maryland Department of Transportation
State Highway Administration

Published in 2008 by the
Maryland Department of Transportation
State Highway Administration
Office of Communications
Editor: Valerie Burnette Edgar, APR

Printed by University of Maryland Printing Services

Photographic Research by Mark Charney

Designed by Integrated Designs, Inc.
idcorpmd.com

Table of Contents

Imagine...

...you're in Maryland 300 years ago

It's 1708

Your highways are made of water. If there's somewhere you want to go that isn't on the Chesapeake Bay or tidal rivers and creeks, then only the stout of heart are going to get there.

It isn't that the General Assembly doesn't care about building and maintaining roads, but they are using a conscripted and unskilled labor source — you. It's an old idea, a long-standing tradition from England's feudal past. But laws don't build roads, people do. That's a problem. There are no standards and limited expertise.

Maryland's first road law was enacted in 1666 and it required counties to create roads passable by horse or foot. In 1704, the General Assembly set standards that required public roads to be cleared to a width of 20 feet and records kept by road overseers recording the number and condition of each county's roads. The road overseers got another duty; they assess fines for those

shirking their road service. On the map, there is a network of public roads leading to towns and markets; with 20-foot-wide roads, you can put a coach or wagon on them. However, the roads are only made of dirt and easily damaged by inclement weather. Maintenance is constantly required and those forced to do it find a feudal tradition from England's past inappropriate in America.

It's 1808

Feudal traditions from England have faded. In fact, England has faded from the American scene as well. It's an age of

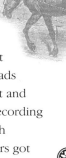

 An early method of making roads happened by necessity. Maryland farmers rolled hogsheads over former animal trails to get their tobacco to market.

private enterprise, and private enterprise takes you from place to place. Across the state, private corporations build and maintain roads for the right to charge a fee for using them. They are called turnpikes. The name comes from a pike or pole that is turned to provide access when the fee is paid.

The turnpike companies provide roads with a base of rocks and smooth surfaces of crushed stone, sand, gravel and even wooden planks. The turnpikes are much better than the old public dirt roads, but they have divided Marylanders into two kinds of citizens — those who can afford to travel on turnpikes and those who can't.

Public roads have taken second place to the private ones, but there is one very big exception. In 1806, President Thomas Jefferson had signed legislation creating the National Road. It is the first interstate road and it begins in Cumberland, Maryland.

 Heavy traffic along the Frederick Pike was a common sight in 1829. The Fairview Inn, or "Three Mile House" as it was commonly called, was among the more popular stopping places. While many weary travelers found accommodations in its private rooms, the less fortunate might be left to catch a few winks on its public floor space.

The National Road will travel west over the Appalachian Mountains and end at the Ohio River in Wheeling (now West Virginia). Commerce will bind the Ohio River Valley with the East Coast. It is as important in defining the new nation as the other Jefferson initiative three years earlier, the Louisiana Purchase.

It's 1908

The turnpike companies are mostly gone, victims of competition from railroads. The National Road has not fared much better, the victim of poor maintenance and erratic funding by Congress. In fact, Congress has given the National Road to the states through which it passes.

Railroads dominate transportation in Maryland and the United States. But railroads have limited routes and not everyone wants to go where the railroads will take them. Farmers find getting their crops to railroad terminals problematic and there is the appearance of a new transportation technology — the automobile.

There are enough automobiles in Maryland that owners are required to register their vehicles and pay a $1 fee to do it. Automobile owners are not happy with Maryland's motley collection of public roads and turnpikes. In 1904, the General Assembly moved in the direction of standards and funding. It authorized funds to be disbursed to counties to help build public roads, if the roads meet standards to be set by the State Geological and Economic Survey.

Few know it at the time, but a precedent is set. In 1908, the State Roads Commission is established. Maryland is taking responsibility for planning a road system and it will use automobile registration fees as means to do it. Hard surface roads will be built, thanks to those who use them.

Today

You drive Thomas Jefferson's dream highway. A 340-foot road-cut takes you through the mountains on the "New Route West," the National Freeway (Interstate 68), and you travel into the Ohio River Valley and the Midwest. But you do more than that. You drive beneath Baltimore's harbor (the Baltimore Harbor Tunnel Thruway or the Fort McHenry Tunnel) and you drive over the Chesapeake Bay (William Preston Lane, Jr. Memorial Bridge). You drive entirely around one city on a circumferential highway (Baltimore's Interstate 695) and do the same thing around another one (the longest stretch, 42.03 miles, of Washington, D.C.'s Interstate 495 is in Maryland). You drive 110 miles from one side of Maryland to the other on Interstate 95 and if you don't get off until it ends, you will either be in Miami, Florida or Houlton, Maine, next to the border with Canada. And the remarkable thing isn't that you do it, but that doing it is so routine that it's unremarkable.

Imagining what life was like in Maryland's past is entertainment, a game that anyone can play. To have a vision of what life might be like in the future requires a special kind of imagination. It's a type of imagination that's not at all common — the vision to see what can be and the will to make it happen. *Moving Maryland Forward* is about people who had that type of imagination and how their vision created one of the finest highway systems in the world.

3

Conestoga wagons were handmade, resulting in varying sizes, but the most common size was 16 feet in length and 4 feet in width. A dip in the center of the Conestoga wagon, forcing the weight of its cargo toward the center, gave it a distinctive profile.

 This 1859 photo demonstrates that Conestoga wagons were used for local travel as well as settling a nation. Here a group of Quakers travel to their quarterly meeting at the old stone meeting house near Western Run at Cockeysville.

The Conestoga Wagon:

In 1927, the B&O Railroad celebrated the centennial of its existence at the Timonium Fairgrounds with "The Fair of the Iron Horse." As part of the celebration, the B&O paid tribute to the Conestoga wagon and the role that it played in developing the nation. Little did the railroad company know that renewed interest in a modern wagon and an open road would soon spell trouble for its future.

High Ways: Early English dirt roads were built by digging two parallel ditches. The removed earth was thrown into the space between the ditches. The resulting raised roadbed was elevated above the ground around it, providing good drainage. This simple method of construction created what was commonly called the "high way."

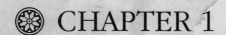

Good Roads Origins

Maryland's first official military road builder, British General Edward Braddock. His name remains an integral part of Maryland road history.

The history of highways in Maryland is the story of where roads go and what travels on them. The first European settlers in Maryland used paths made by animals and Native Americans as their roads. Since hunting game was a source of food, and Indian paths often led to navigable or drinkable water, these pathways were highly valued.

In 1666, the General Assembly ordered the counties to maintain pathways to a standard of accessibility by foot and horseback. These maintained pathways were the good roads of early Maryland history.

The needs of commerce changed things in the 18th century. The Maryland road law of 1704 required roads to be made wide enough so coaches and wagons could use them. Road overseers marked the roads to ferries, churches and towns. County residents performed the tasks of digging up tree roots and clearing out new growth.

However, war — not commerce — was behind the greatest road-building effort in Maryland's colonial history. It was the result of the French and Indian War (1754-1763). British Major General Edward Braddock cut a 12-foot-wide road beginning at the junction of Wills Creek and the Potomac River in Maryland to bring his army, artillery and supplies 110 miles over the Appalachian Mountains to fight the French and their Indian allies in the upper Ohio River Valley. Braddock was killed during the war and his body buried beneath "Braddock's Road."

If not for evolving technology, there would be no need for more than dirt roads. The evolving technology was coaches and wagons. Coaches and wagons were the big movers of their day, but they traveled on heavy iron rims wrapped around large wooden wheels, and they cut deep ruts in dirt roads. Perhaps the greatest offender was the

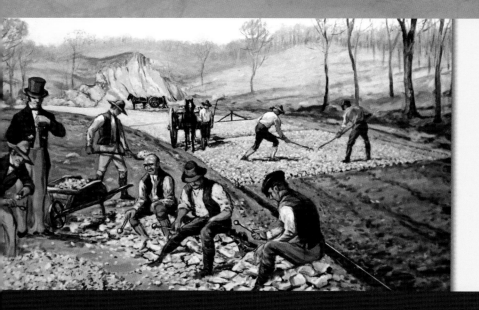

 "The First American Macadam Road." Constructing the National Road between Hagerstown and Boonsboro in 1823.

Macadam

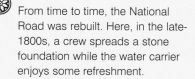 Maryland road builders used these mallets to break rocks for the construction of macadam roads.

What was the greatest natural challenge to Maryland's roads? It wasn't the dense forest that awaited the first settlers. Trees were downed and stubs and roots grubbed out. It wasn't the sandy soil of the Eastern Shore or the clay soil of Southern Maryland or the Western Shore. Oyster shells were layered on top of sand and rocks on top of clay. It wasn't the hilly Piedmont or the mountainous Appalachians. Roads followed hilly terrain and Native Americans had made footpaths in the gaps between mountains. It wasn't fire. Fire scorched the earth, but had barely any impact on roads.

The greatest natural challenge to Maryland roads was water in all its forms. The genius of the macadam road was based on the realization that water, not wear, was the road's greatest adversary. A macadam road only 10 inches deep would outlast a stone road twice as deep, because water couldn't penetrate the macadamized road's tightly packed foundation.

This painting by Carl Rakeman (above) depicts workmen laboring on the turnpike road between Hagerstown and Boonsboro, Maryland. They are breaking stones into smaller ones. The final layers of rocks on macadamized roads had to be very small, no more than two inches in circumference. Two-inch brass rings were used to measure the size of stones, but a quick and expedient alternative was the "mouth test." Stones that wouldn't fit in your mouth were too big.

From time to time, the National Road was rebuilt. Here, in the late-1800s, a crew spreads a stone foundation while the water carrier enjoys some refreshment.

Conestoga wagon. The Conestoga wagon evolved in the hilly countryside of the Conestoga River Valley of Pennsylvania. It was far wider than the common farm wagon and able to carry heavier loads. It featured large wheels that allowed the wagon to pass over tree stumps and ford shallow streams.

Conestoga wagons, often drawn by four horses, were a common sight on Maryland roads. They carried farmers' produce to markets and manufactured goods back to the farms. They were the tractor-trailers of Maryland's roads for 100 years (1750 to 1850) and as time passed they got bigger, over 20 feet in length, and carried heavier loads drawn by six-horse teams.

What the Conestoga wagon did best, carrying heavy loads of up to five tons, was the undoing of Maryland's network of county-based dirt roads. It cut ruts in the roads, making them impassable during the winter months and after heavy rains. The counties were unable to supply the needed maintenance to keep the roads functional.

The road-building technology that evolved to meet the challenge posed by the Conestoga wagon was the macadam road. The principle of the macadamized road, developed by Scotsman John McAdam, was to dig a sloped subgrade flanked by drainage ditches. Layers of broken stones were placed in tight patterns and covered with small two-inch stones that were compacted. The result was a water-resistant surface. Rain and snow drained off the sloped surface of compressed stone and was carried away by drainage ditches. You could travel a macadam road at any time of the year.

 Before the advent of a state roads system, private turnpike companies chartered sections of main trunk line roads from county governments. While macadam roads were the preferred method of construction, quality of road surface and toll payments varied widely. Historian William Hollifield identified this toll gate as being on Frederick Road near Ellicott City.

 The earliest road builders faced difficult challenges establishing roads across rugged terrain without modern machinery. This early 20th century photograph shows how roads were graded using horse-drawn equipment.

 These stock certificates represent 42 shares in the Baltimore Reisterstown Turnpike Co. and 100 shares in the Baltimore Yorktown Turnpike Co.

The problem with the macadam road was that it required a skill level greater than the counties' citizens possessed. In 1804, the General Assembly devised an ingenious way to solve this dilemma, by marrying private enterprise with public need.

Turnpike companies were awarded state charters to build roads and collect fees for their efforts. A tollgate with a pike or pole blocked access to their roads. The distance at which the tollgates could be placed, and fees collected, was stipulated in the turnpike company's charter.

The timing was fortuitous. Two years later, in 1806, Thomas Jefferson signed legislation authorizing the first interstate highway, a National Road from Cumberland, on the Potomac River, over the Allegheny Front of the Appalachian Mountains, to Wheeling, Virginia (later West Virginia) on the Ohio River. By 1818, the first national highway had linked two great rivers, and then in piecemeal spasms it continued west across Ohio, Indiana and Illinois. But it didn't go east.

That was the impetus for the Maryland General Assembly to charter the most

important of its turnpike companies, the Cumberland Turnpike Company. It reached Cumberland in 1820, with only a few gaps from Cumberland to Baltimore. State banks owned a majority of the company's stock, thereby earning the turnpike's nickname, the "Bank Road."

The attraction of the turnpike, and why you would pay to be on one, was the macadamized surface. Coaches and wagons didn't create ruts. In fact, they were constantly compacting the stones that most macadamized roads were built upon. The "good road" was the macadam road, and the first macadamized road in the United States was a 10-mile section of the Bank Road.

A preview of today's interstate trucking was a team of horses pulling a Conestoga wagon over Maryland's turnpikes and the National Road. Until the middle of the 19th century, this was a viable way to transport agricultural products from the West to Baltimore and manufactured goods from the East to the Ohio Valley. The census of 1830 revealed that Baltimore had surpassed Philadelphia to become the second largest city in the United States, and somewhere between 1830 and 1840, Baltimore became the

second American city to surpass the 100,000-population mark (New York City was the first).

Propelled by its busy port and access to the West, Baltimore would remain the second largest city in the United States for the next 20 years. However, interstate commerce in Maryland during the remainder of the 19th century did not belong to roads; it belonged to the rails. In 1827, the Baltimore and Ohio Railroad Company was chartered. Its railroad tracks reached Cumberland in 1842 and Chicago in 1874.

The railroad dominated interstate commerce, but at the same time that B&O trains were riding the rails to Chicago, a German engineer, Gottlieb Daimler, was working on a four-cycle gasoline engine. When he perfected it, another German, Karl Benz, mounted it on a bicycle with a chain-drive in 1885. In the United States, in 1893, two bicycle mechanics, Charles and Frank Duryea, drove their own "horseless carriage" powered by a gasoline motor. The federal government had long abandoned the National Road and seemed to have little interest in getting into the roads business again. Only

 THE *Postal* SERVICE

linked isolated regions to the larger world thanks to Rural Free Delivery.

Lawrence "Speedy" Bittinger carries the U.S. Mail from Grantsville, Maryland westbound over Negro Mountain.

"object-lesson" roads were built, and these were not built as highways, but as demonstrations of road-building techniques by the Department of Agriculture. Maryland's General Assembly was also more interested in studying roads than building them. To carry out those studies, they relied on the State Geological and Economic Survey, which authored a series of reports on roads and suitable road-building material.

Apart from the U.S. Army Corps of Engineers, there were few formally trained engineers in the 19th century. Since roads were mainly used for local travel, the actual building of roads was left to the local jurisdictions, incorporated towns and counties. Men who typically had no formal training in building them constructed the roads. Best practices consisted of suggestions passed on by the scientists at the Maryland Geological Survey.

At the turn of the 20th century, few visionaries saw a transportation revolution in the making. Effective lobbying for good roads came from an odd alliance: farmers and bicyclists.

Cycling was made safe with the introduction of the "safety" design, consisting of two wheels of the same size; it was made comfortable with the use of air-filled tires and padded seats. Bicycling became the hobby of city dwellers wanting to venture out into the countryside for recreation. The League of American Wheelmen was founded in 1880 to promote the biking hobby. The name of its communications vehicle, *Good Roads Magazine*, is evidence of its primary objective.

Farmers might seem an unusual ally of urban bicyclists, but they had an interest in good roads as well. For most of the 19th century, rural area residents had to travel to nearby towns or city post offices to get their mail. Urban dwellers had mail delivered to their homes since the Civil War, as tradition has it, so that the relatives of the dead would not have to find out about the deaths of their loved ones in a public place. Rural Free Delivery (RFD) began in 1896, but only if you lived on a passable road. What was essentially an equality issue in delivering the mail did more than provide equality between urban and rural residents. It created a connection between building

roads, which was not a federal function, and one that was, delivering the mail. The pleas of bicyclists and farmers started the good roads movement of the 20th century. In 1904, Baltimore County farmer and activist Samuel Shoemaker pushed a "state-aid" road bill through the General Assembly. The appropriation of $200,000 was to be used as state matching grants, distributed through the Maryland Geological Survey, to those counties that built macadam roads. The Maryland Geological Survey, to the chagrin of county commissioners, required exacting standards for road construction.

Bicyclists and farmers scored gains in moving Maryland into the road-building business. Demonstrations on how to build modern roads were conducted, pamphlets were published on the material with which to do it and matching grants awarded for "state-aid" roads. As the government tested the waters of road building, Henry Ford dreamed of an affordable automobile.

THE *Automobile*

Early car manufacturers struggled to find a word to describe their product. The Anglo-American title of "horseless carriage" described early cars by what they were not – carriages with horses. The French coined a term to describe them by what they were, a self-propelled means of moving or automobile.

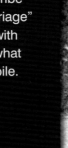 Automobiles on the National Pike, looking west past Keyser's Ridge.

THE *Good Roads* MOVEMENT

 A Good Roads Committee from Johnstown, a Calvert County village near Solomons, celebrates upgrades to a local road.

GOOD ROADS COMMITTEE
JOHNSTOWN CHAMBER COMMERCE

BALTIMORE COUNTY
THE GARDEN SPOT OF MARYLAND.
FIRST TO BUILD A CONCRETE ROAD — FIRST TO BUILD A CONCRETE BRIDGE.

IT'S GOOD ROADS HAVE ENHANCED PROPERTY VALUES IN ALL SECTIONS.
WHERE FIELDS STOOD BEFORE, PROGRESSIVE DEVELOPMENTS NOW DOT THE LANDSCAPE.

 The Federal Bureau of Public Roads was not the only agency promoting good roads in the early 20th century. Baltimore County had an advanced good road improvement and promotional program. The county became a primary source of engineering talent for the Maryland Geological Survey and later the State Roads Commission.

Samuel M. Shoemaker was a Baltimore County dairy farmer who was one of the leading activists in the movement to "get the farmers out of the mud." The so-called "Shoemaker Act" of 1904 set the precedent of offering state grants to local governments to build roads, based on standards set by the Geological Survey.

Along with farmers, cyclists (above) were some of the earliest advocates for good roads. Club-sponsored tours and races were frequently reported in local newspapers. This 1891 bicycle rally in Hagerstown features the pennants and banners of a number of regional clubs.

While Maryland led many states in its progressive advocacy for good roads, Jim Crow laws and prejudice prevented its African-American citizens from enjoying the same privileges as their white counterparts. Such prejudice denied Charles Seymour Diggs acceptance to a private Maryland driving school. An employee and horse trainer at Samuel Shoemaker's Burnside Farm, Diggs was sent to Detroit, Michigan, where he received driver's lessons and later worked as Shoemaker's personal chauffeur.

Farmers were an important part of the Good Roads Movement. Working long hours at their trade, their ability to haul heavy loads to market was critical to their livelihood.

In 1900, the total production of automobiles in the United States was 4,192 machines. They were all handmade and cost between $3,000 and $12,000. Ten years later, 187,000 automobiles were produced on American assembly lines at less than a third of the price of the least expensive vehicle in 1900. Automobiles were the most formidable challenge to Maryland roads since the Conestoga wagon.

 Governor Austin Lane Crothers, father of the Maryland State Roads system.

During his term as Governor (1908-1912), Austin Lane Crothers pushed the General Assembly to adopt a Progressive agenda of public service experts to oversee the people's business. The result was a State Bank Commissioner, a Public Service Commission and the State Roads Commission.

The State Roads Commission was given seven years to create a state road system by expanding state aid to county roads, purchasing privately owned turnpikes and building state roads. The "seven-year plan" promised to connect all of Maryland's county seats with paved roads.

Roads were increasingly important, but not the unpaved macadam roads of turnpike days. Macadamized stone surface roads were suited to slow-moving coaches and wagons, but not to rubber wheels moving "horseless carriages" at twice their speed or more. Rubber tires generated heat and suction. They pulled small stones out of unpaved roadways and left dust in their wake.

What coaches and wagons had done to dirt roads, automobiles did to unpaved macadamized roads. They made them obsolete. No one knew that at the beginning of the 20th century. Automobiles were a novelty enjoyed by the rich and almost no one envisioned the transportation explosion about to occur.

The automobile arrived on the American scene at a time known as the "Progressive Era." The period encompasses the presidencies of Theodore Roosevelt through Woodrow Wilson. "Progressivism" is an umbrella term for many different reform movements, but the thread that runs through it is the belief in a scientific approach to problem solving and the use of the government as the agent to do it.

For most of the 19th century, being a party loyalist was the only criterion for a government job. The Progressives wanted to turn that political equation on its head. To them, government jobs existed to solve problems and having the skills to do the job trumped party affiliation.

Austin Lane Crothers, the son of a Cecil County farmer, was a former Democratic State Senator. In 1907, he successfully campaigned for governor with a Progressive agenda of reforms, which included good roads. In 1908, the General Assembly responded by creating the State Roads Commission (SRC) and on April 30, Governor Crothers swore in its five members with the Governor himself serving as an ex-officio member. By legislative fiat, all things involving roads gravitated to the SRC, including the highway work of the Geological Survey and $5 million to create a state roads system.

From his home and studio in Grantsville, Maryland photographer Leo Beachy found himself fascinated by a developing theme — car and road culture. Here relatives of his, "the Otto girls," demonstrate their unique method of fixing a flat.

Ford Model Ts at a hill climb in Loch Raven, 1921.

The Model T made its debut in 1908 and sold for $825. By 1924, the year the ten millionth Model T was produced, you could buy it for $290. Henry Ford did not invent the automobile, but he revolutionized the assembly production process, making it affordable for the average Marylander.

THE *Model* "T"

The Brooks family is reported to be the first proud owner of an automobile in northern Baltimore County, around 1906 to 1907. Mr. and Mrs. William C. Brooks (far right) and their family.

The Baltimore Fire of 1904 provided Marylanders with the impetus they needed to create public works commissions, both in city and state government. Four years later, the Union Trust building at Charles and Lexington Streets would be restored and serve as the first home for the State Roads Commission.

William Bullock Clark

Dr. William Bullock Clark was one of the original State Roads Commissioners. He was also Superintendent of the State Geological and Economic Survey, founder of the Maryland State Weather Service and a professor at Johns Hopkins University.

The first Chairman of the SRC, John Tucker was a native of Cecil County and friend of Governor Crothers. He worked as a banker before heading up the new agency. When determining the first state road system, Tucker traveled the state mostly by boat and train–an indication of how much a good road system was needed.

John Tucker

Tarmac

Covering a macadam road with tar bound the top layer of road material into a solid surface. The resulting "paved" road held surface stones in place and reduced the dust created by automobile tires. It was called a tarmac. Tarmac roads did not hold up well when used by heavier vehicles, like trucks. After World War I, concrete and asphalt were the preferable alternatives to tar.

 In 1910, a road crew in Westminster spreads tar sprayed from hoses over a macadam road.

 Using horses instead of manpower, this 1913 operation in Rockville sprays oil over a resurfaced macadam road.

This Johns Hopkins campus building on Howard Street served many uses before being torn down. At one time it was home to the Maryland Weather Station as well as the Maryland Geological Survey. When the Survey handed its responsibilities over to the State Roads Commission, the building became home to the SRC's scientific pursuits as its first materials and testing laboratory.

The State Roads Commission's ties to the Geological Survey gave them access to Dr. William Bullock Clark, who was its superintendent. Dr. Clark was a scientist with expertise in the branch of geology dealing with rock strata, and a professor at Johns Hopkins University. Clark was appointed as one of the original State Roads Commissioners. This unique entanglement, through the multiple employments of Dr. Clark, gave the work of the commission both the aura of science and the imprimatur of government. That was important, since the commission's credibility with the General Assembly depended on maintaining the progressive image of standing above politics and standing for technocratic expertise.

In 1912, the State Roads Commission made a full and comprehensive report to the General Assembly. It was its first official statement of accountability and it pulled no punches. The commission, citing previous studies by the Geological Survey, labeled county-based road building "antiquated" and a "positive handicap to the development of the State." The commission also quoted the Geological Survey's conclusion that "an efficient system of main roads and feeders covering the whole state is desirable from every standpoint." If there was any difference of opinion between the commission and the Geological Survey, it wasn't detectable, perhaps not surprising given the key role of Dr. Clark in both organizations.

The Geological Survey couldn't tell the counties where to build roads, but it could require them to build roads to the highest standards of the day. The relationship between county officials and Dr. Clark and his staff of engineers was not always cordial. In one of the Geological Survey's reports, it opined, "The elimination of political influences from the disbursement of the road money is perhaps too much of a reform to expect, but it is not too much to hope that at no distant time it will be found to be good politics to make good roads." When the road-building activities of the Geological Survey were put under the State Roads Commission, Dr. Clark listed among its assets the "appreciation by the public of the good roads movement."

Dedicated funding for Maryland's roads began in 1904, but the Automobile Law of 1910 introduced the concept that those who used the roads should pay for them. The law required all motorists operating vehicles on Maryland's growing network of state and state-aided highways to procure a fee-based operator's license, a certificate of registration and a license plate. The income from these fees was dedicated to the construction and maintenance of roads. John Hendrick, a District of Columbia resident, sued the state.

Mr. Hendrick had been arrested and fined $15 for operating his vehicle without an operator's license, certificate of registration or a license plate. Hendrick challenged the constitutionality of Maryland's Automobile Law. The case was eventually heard by the United States Supreme Court, which decided in 1915 (Hendrick v. State of Maryland) that Maryland's Automobile Law did not violate the Interstate Commerce Clause of the Constitution. In a ringing endorsement, the Supreme Court concluded "there can be no serious doubt that where a state at its own expense furnishes special facilities for the use of those engaged in commerce, interstate as well as domestic, it may exact compensation therefore."

In the history of Maryland road building, one can see the story of people who had the vision to see what good roads could be. There were farmer activists like Samuel Shoemaker who saw a day when farmers could get "out of the mud." There were Progressive politicians like Governor Austin Lane Crothers who saw that a good road system must follow a plan and envisioned a goal of linking all of the county seats with ribbons of asphalt. There were men of science like Dr. William Bullock Clark. There was recognition by the General Assembly that roads would be used predominantly by the automobile and there was acknowledgement by the courts that the state could apply user-fees to build its highways.

Of course, no list of Maryland's road building visionaries would be complete without mention of the State Roads Commission, the SRC commissioners themselves, the chief engineers and the legions of workers who transformed that vision into reality.

Heavy use of trucks during the war and concern for road conditions caused the SRC to measure truck weights with loadometers. Excess weight was removed and dumped at the roadside.

 In 1918, Leo Beachy recorded increased Army truck traffic along his beloved National Road. Here the Co. A 105 "supply train" stops to refuel on its way to Eastern ports.

During World War I, military trucks rode on solid rubber tires and were capable of carrying up to five tons of supplies to ships waiting at East Coast ports like Baltimore. The first roads built by the SRC were not designed to stand up to this heavy traffic, and they suffered serious damage as a result. After the war, considerable effort was expended to rebuild these damaged roads. New tire designs with inflatable rubber tires allowed trucks to travel over roadways with less damage.

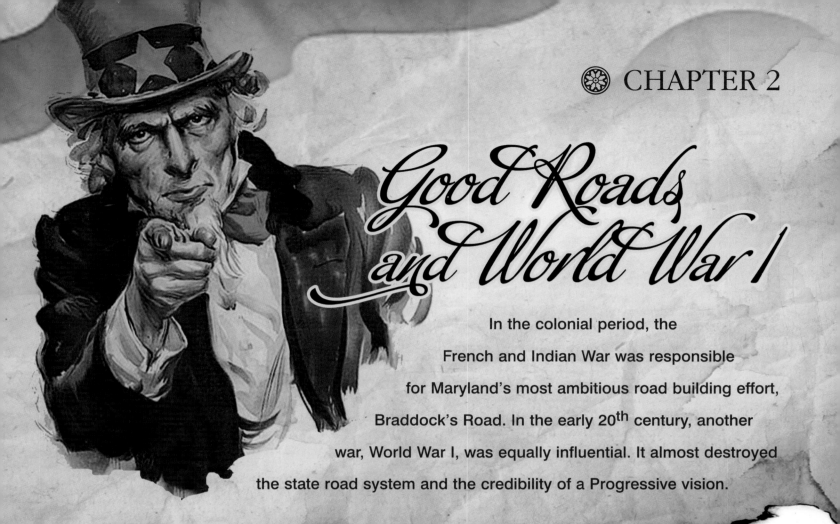

CHAPTER 2

Good Roads and World War I

In the colonial period, the French and Indian War was responsible for Maryland's most ambitious road building effort, Braddock's Road. In the early 20th century, another war, World War I, was equally influential. It almost destroyed the state road system and the credibility of a Progressive vision.

On the eve of the United States' participation in World War I, the State Roads Commission met the General Assembly mandate to create a statewide highway system. It was cobbled together by purchase (private turnpikes), inheritance (county roads) and industry (state-built roads). A network of paved roads connected every county seat, and it had been done in only seven years. The *Baltimore Sun* called it "a primary road system ahead of any state."

Common sense would suggest that two great cities, only 30 miles apart, would be linked by a road, but even before there was a Baltimore or a Washington, D.C., there were dirt paths linking the Patapsco and the Potomac. These pathways were county-maintained roads of poor quality. The 1704 General Assembly requirement of 20-foot-wide roads opened county roads to wagons and coaches. They made the harrowing trip over ruts and stumps and frequently had to be pulled out of heavy mud. In 1820, a private turnpike company was chartered to build a macadamized road that served as the nation's only entrance into Washington, D.C. from

Baltimore. The turnpike folded in 1865 and the pieces of its roadway became county roads.

In 1906, the Maryland General Assembly appropriated state funds for a paved road, to be built by the Geological Survey, linking Baltimore and Washington, D.C. When the highway work of the Geological Survey came under the State Roads Commission, the construction of the first paved state road began. Its name was State Road No.1.

THE STORY OF *Washington* BOULEVARD

State Road No. 1 set a precedent. Before State Road No.1, each county built its own roads. State Road No.1 was Maryland's road, a new road and a new concept. When it was completed in 1915, it was one of the finest paved roads in the country. It was also something never before seen in Maryland, a road that was a destination in itself. Marylanders drove their automobiles on State Road No. 1 for the sheer experience of riding a long stretch of paved highway.

State Road No. 1 was the jewel in the crown of the new state road system. Three years after it was opened, it was a war casualty, part of the price paid to make "the world safe for democracy." Heavy World War I vintage trucks traveling to Baltimore's port, or the Army's Fort Meade, cracked its pavement and the winter of 1917-18 left it torn and full of potholes.

State Road No.1 was rebuilt after the war. It emerged from reconstruction as a key part of a link in an interstate system of state roads running from Fort Kent, Maine to Key West, Florida.

State Road No.1 came back as U.S. 1, but the passage had taken a price — the loss of innocence. By 1925, 6,000 automobiles and trucks whizzed by each day. It was widened from 20 feet to 40 feet and expanded from two to four lanes. Traffic increased threefold and with traffic came consumerism. One thousand billboards crowded Maryland's section of U.S. 1 at an average of 39 billboards per mile by 1934.

By the 1930s U.S. 1 had many names. Sometimes referred to as "Bloody Mary" and other times as "Billboard Boulevard," the road had a reputation for danger and distraction. The State Roads Commission invested in road surface upgrades, widening and elimination of dangerous curves. Despite these efforts, U.S. 1 continued as one of the most crash-prone highways in the nation.

Early 20th century road signs along the Baltimore-Washington Boulevard were not constructed to be read at high speeds. Signs such as this one along State Road No. 1 indicate that drivers of horse and carriage as well as horseless carriage had time to ponder travel directions. The first Maryland speed limit on the open road was set at 10 mph in 1904. By 1914 it had been raised to 25 mph.

 The true pioneers of the State Roads Commission may have been the surveyors who set out from Baltimore to chart existing Maryland roads. These men braved long stays away from home, inclement weather and rugged terrain. This 1913 photo portrays a survey party crew on Port Tobacco Road in La Plata. Standing left to right, Surveyor Ellis C. Graham and Survey Party Chief Leonard E. Major. Seated are Rodmen William M. Brown and Walter A. Friend along with "Axman" F. S. Deckens. The young driver of the ox team is unidentified.

Life magazine called U.S. 1 the Main Street of the East Coast, but driving on Maryland's part of Main Street was the opposite of everything that State Road No.1 used to be. Traffic patterns moved to commercial enticements and driving was chaotic and accident prone. No one would drive on U.S. 1 for the joy of the experience.

The roadway for State Road No.1 is still U.S. 1, but the goal of pleasurable driving between Baltimore and Washington, D.C. did not return until the middle of the 20th century. A few miles to the east, the Baltimore-Washington Parkway parallels the route of old State Road No.1. Two separate ribbons of concrete gently move travelers to their destination in Baltimore or Washington through a park-like setting of trees. The builders of the Baltimore-Washington Parkway learned a lesson from the history of U.S. 1. It has no billboards hawking roadside attractions to travelers.

The day-to-day operation of the Maryland state road system was in the hands of Henry G. Shirley, the Commission's Chief Engineer. Shirley is a legend in American highway history. He was the executive secretary of the Federal Highway Council, a founding member and the first president of the American Association of State Highway Officials, president of the American Road Builders Association and Virginia's State Highway Commissioner. However, in 1912, he was the new 38-year-old Chief Engineer of the State Roads Commission.

Henry G. Shirley became the State Roads Commission's Chief Engineer in 1912. He completed Governor Austin Lane Crothers' "seven year plan" and supervised the construction and maintenance of Maryland's first highway system on the eve of World War I.

Pictured left in a 1914 photograph are the founding members of the American Association of State Highway Officials (AASHO), including Henry Shirley, its first president (first row, seated second from the left). Shirley's role in founding AASHO was indicative of a growing preference for federal involvement in road building, previously a local responsibility.

The Henry G. Shirley Memorial Highway, a key part of I-95 and I-395 in Virginia, is named in his honor.

Henry G. Shirley

Shirley was the epitome of the Progressive problem solver. He held a civil engineering degree from Virginia Military Institute and a doctorate in science from the University of Maryland. One of Shirley's first acts was the division of the state into eight districts, each run by a Resident Engineer who was responsible for construction and maintenance standards. The Resident Engineers were given motorcycles and ordered to oversee the roads in their districts.

Wearing goggles and leggings, Resident Engineers appointed by Shirley tracked maintenance work performed by road patrolmen. Shirley knew that building paved roads was only half of the job; the other half was maintaining them.

Maintaining Maryland's newly-paved macadamized roads was the job of a small army of patrolmen. Each of them was given a cap with "State Patrolman" marked in gold letters and assigned a territory of four to eight miles of road. The advantage of the patrolman system was the speed of road repairs. As soon as a patrolman sighted a developing pothole, he would mark it off with a red flag, commence filling it in with a bituminous material like asphalt and cover it with stone chips. Then he would beat the mixture into a compact patch. This was good for the roads and a good

advertisement for passing motorists watching the State Roads Commission taking care of the highways that they had paid registration fees to drive upon.

From 1908 until 1917 were the halcyon days of Maryland roads. Men of science — modern men, progressive men — had turned local dirt roads into paved highways, the envy of other states and a national model. Bicyclists used them for transportation and recreation; motorists traveled from one part of the state to another with confidence that they would get there; farmers delivered crops to railroad stations and Rural Free Delivery brought information to those who lived in isolation.

SRC workers with mule cart repairing state roads. With the establishment of district offices, Salisbury Resident Engineer William F. "Buck" Childs recalled his first SRC-issued vehicle, a mule cart similar to that shown here. Childs earned $133.33 per month as Resident Engineer of the Salisbury district. The average salary for a district engineer in 1915 was $150 per month.

World War I surplus such as motorcycles and trucks were given to the SRC by the U.S. Army. Resident engineers graduated from mule carts to motorcycles with sidecars.

SRC patrolman preparing to patch a road with tar. After the patrolman completed his task, a Resident Engineer followed behind to inspect his work.

THE *Road* CONTRACTORS

Patrick Flanigan (standing far right) started his contracting business in 1885 by running a sewer line down Baltimore City's Charles Street and charging people to use it. When the city took over that line, Flanigan switched to road building. His company constructed roads of Belgian block, macadam, Trinidad asphalt, hot-mix asphalt and concrete, and the company continues that road-building tradition today. Here, a Flanigan road crew prepares to add a coat of Trinidad asphalt to a macadam surface.

Prior to World War I, building roads was dependent on manual labor using the same tools — picks, shovels, hammers, sledges and scrapers — that would have been familiar to the ancient Romans. It was a hard, labor-intensive job. Even the State Roads Commission's inventory of pre-war power equipment consisted of only a few stone-crushers and steamrollers, but that was an environment ripe with opportunities for first-generation immigrants and sons of former slaves who had little more than labor to offer.

Patrick Flanigan is a case in point. He was born in Ireland and immigrated to the United States during the Civil War. After a stint at running a general store in Baltimore, Flanigan left for a business that four generations of his family have never given up, road building.

Few would suspect that those who did some of Maryland's dirtiest work would be called upon to help save Baltimore, but on a bitterly cold Sunday morning in February 1904, that's what happened.

A fire started in the Hurst Building, a wholesale drygoods house in the heart of the business district, and soon became a roaring conflagration threatening to burn down the entire city. Baltimore firefighters were overwhelmed. Washington, D.C. firefighters came to help, but found their hoses wouldn't fit Baltimore's hydrants. The call for help went out to firefighters in Philadelphia and New York. In the meantime, P. Flanigan & Sons offered a road-building tool that might block the fire until help arrived — dynamite.

"My great grandfather, and my grandfather and his two brothers started dynamiting buildings in advance of the fire to slow its spread," Pierce Flanigan recalled. "I remember my Great Uncle Ed telling a story that he was walking down the street with a half of a case of dynamite over his shoulder when a glowing ember the size of his fist landed on it. There was a 50-50 chance it would explode, but obviously it just burned out because he lived to tell the story."

More than 70 city blocks and 1,500 buildings were lost, but only two years later the *Baltimore News-American* newspaper reported the city had risen from the ashes. Patrick Flanigan and his kin were there, building new roads to replace the ones that had been destroyed in the "Great Baltimore Fire."

THE *Parker Family* AND THEIR TRUCKS

The founder of the family hauling business, African-American Charlie Parker, Sr. got his start hauling away debris from the "Great Baltimore Fire" of 1904 in a mule dump cart. Parker's mule dump cart became a truck and the debris from burned buildings became the coal to heat the buildings that replaced them. What others found useless, coal cinders, were hauled away by Parker and sold to cinder block makers and road builders. Charlie Parker, Sr. became a well-known contract hauler in road building in early 20th century Maryland, and his company a steady employer of African-Americans living in South Baltimore.

 The Parker family and their fleet of trucks, circa late 1920s.

A tarmac-paving train appears in these Western Maryland photos ready to improve an existing macadam road. Tarmac from the famed Pitch Lake in Trinidad arrived in sacks to be reheated in mobile boilers and then spread along the road surface. Sacks can be seen here resting atop the caravan of equipment.

Another view of the tarmac-paving train reveals a boiler marked with SRC insignia, indicating that not all road work was contracted out. SRC forces were still experimenting with new methods.

Improvise AND Adapt

On the Eastern Shore where soils are sandy and base rock for asphalt is scarce, SRC maintenance staff learned to "improvise and adapt," a phrase still heard among SHA workers today. Here, a worker grades a road with oyster shells from Eastern Shore canning factories. Continuously pulverized by traffic, oyster shells made a smooth-riding surface but needed constant attention. Road workers had to battle rutting from narrow tires.

THE FATHER OF *Asphalt*

If John McAdam is the "father" of modern road design, then is there a father figure for what goes on top of most Maryland roads today — asphalt? Some might say that Edward J. DeSmedt deserves the honor. He was a Belgian-born chemist who in the 1870s devised the successful formula for the first hot-mixed blend of asphalt binder and aggregate. Others would nominate Frederick J. Warren, an American inventor, whose patented "Warrenite" hot-mix was the paving choice of road builders at the turn of the 20th century.

Pennsylvania Avenue in Washington, D.C. was among the first beneficiaries of a "man-made" asphalt topping.

However, the man who did the paving, American entrepreneur Amzi Lorenzo Barber, might say it isn't the inventor of the asphalt formula, but he who provided the asphalt that deserves the title of "father of asphalt."

Barber gained control of the volcanic pitch lakes in Trinidad and Venezuela at the turn of the 20th century and crafted a conglomerate of asphalt-paving companies into the Asphalt Company of America. He boasted that he was "identified with the laying of more pavements, or the furnishing of material therefore, than any other person in the history of the world."

 What later became known as asphalt was first referred to in Maryland as bituminous concrete, bituminous paving or sheet asphalt. Its first use in the state occurred on the Philadelphia Road, MD 7, in about 1918. The process retained the use of a macadam base over which was placed a one-inch binder and finally a one and one-half inch topcoat. This 1922 photo (above) shows workers spreading a topcoat on the Boonsboro-Shepherdstown Pike, modern day MD 34 in Washington County.

Rain and snow were tamed with macadamized roadbeds sealed with asphalt. However, rain and snow are not the only forms of water to challenge road builders.

Maryland is a state laced with rivers and streams, and it's cut down the middle by the Chesapeake Bay. In the colonial period, when water was the highway, Maryland was blessed. On the eve of World War I, the blessing was bridges. In colonial days, wooden bridges abounded across Maryland's streams. The Maryland colony was heavily forested and wooden bridges were cheap and easy to construct. The best of them were covered to protect the roadways from deterioration. However, even the best wooden bridges did not last long. Stone-arch bridges, which were the wooden bridges' successor, were works of art built for the ages, but not for the automobile and truck. They were too narrow.

The pioneers of good bridge design in Maryland were railroad builders. They went beyond stone-arch bridges to viaducts built of cast iron, wrought iron and later, steel. Metal bridges were prefabricated at foundries, shipped piecemeal in trains to construction sites and assembled. This produced uniformity of product, high quality and low costs, which appealed to railroad companies and their shareholders.

It was natural for the State Roads Commission to look to railroad men when it came to building bridges for automobiles and trucks. John E. Greiner, a former Baltimore and Ohio Railroad engineer, designed the best of these early bridges, the Hanover Street Bridge, in 1916.

SPANNING MARYLAND *Waterways*

The Bollman truss bridge, constructed of wrought iron, was an infrequent but elegant part of the Maryland landscape. This one was located in Baltimore County at Lake Roland in 1886.

Maryland counties were dotted with simple wooden and covered bridges well into the 20th century. This timber-beam Burr arch bridge built in 1865 crosses the Little Gunpowder Falls and links Baltimore and Harford Counties.

Pictured left, the Casselman River Bridge in Grantsville, Garrett County, is a classic example of the stone-arched bridge. Built in 1815 by John Bing, this bridge is now a National Historic Landmark. It was part of the National Road and its 80-foot span was the largest stone arch in America when the bridge was built. It was continuously in use until 1933. This Leo Beachy photograph entitled "Repairing the Old National Pike Bridge" dates to 1911.

The Hanover Street Bridge did more than replace a wooden bridge across the Patapsco River at the historic entry into Baltimore from the south. It demonstrated that reinforced concrete could combine the pleasing aspect of the stone-arched bridge by using local materials and do it with the uniformity of design, quality and cost effectiveness of metal railroad viaducts.

No one would have predicted that the assassination of an archduke, Franz Ferdinand, in a place few Marylanders had heard of, Sarajevo, would destroy Maryland's road-building accomplishments.

In 1917, the United States entered World War I by doing what it would do again a generation later — supply war materials to its European allies. In 1917, the Army ordered 30,000 trucks from automobile manufacturers in Detroit. The Quartermaster General decided that the trucks would be driven from the factories to East Coast ports.

On January 3, 1918, 29 vehicles of the first overland convoy rolled into Baltimore and more would follow. Supply-laden trucks with solid rubber wheels tore to pieces the thinly-paved highways on which they traveled. For Maryland to impose weight limits on the

military trucks traveling its roads, especially during wartime, was unthinkable. The jewel of the state highway system, Washington Boulevard, took the worst beating because it was the route to the Army's Fort Meade.

The core of Progressivism was the belief that science could and should be used to solve problems. The mystique of the State Roads Commission was that it could build and maintain modern paved highways better than the counties, perhaps better than anyone in the United States. World War I demonstrated that even good roads go bad when the vehicles using them change.

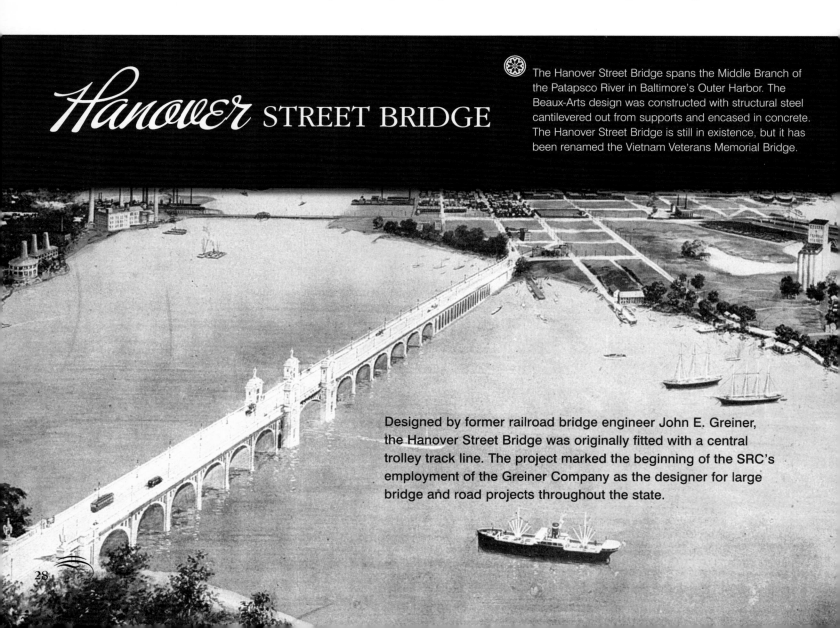

Hanover STREET BRIDGE

The Hanover Street Bridge spans the Middle Branch of the Patapsco River in Baltimore's Outer Harbor. The Beaux-Arts design was constructed with structural steel cantilevered out from supports and encased in concrete. The Hanover Street Bridge is still in existence, but it has been renamed the Vietnam Veterans Memorial Bridge.

Designed by former railroad bridge engineer John E. Greiner, the Hanover Street Bridge was originally fitted with a central trolley track line. The project marked the beginning of the SRC's employment of the Greiner Company as the designer for large bridge and road projects throughout the state.

SRC engineers had not anticipated the heavy military trucks of World War I, but neither had the railroads. In fact, the railroads didn't see the truck coming. They saw trucks as a way to get freight to railroad stations, not as competition. When the federal government expressed an interest in demonstrating the latest road-building techniques, the railroads even volunteered "Good Roads Trains" to take government engineers and their equipment from state to state to build demonstration roads.

After World War I, the humble truck, previously relegated to bringing goods to and from railroad stations, became a mighty competitor to the railroads and a challenge for highway builders. The year the war ended, 525,000 non-military trucks were traveling the nation's roads. This was an increase of approximately 40 percent from when World War I had begun.

In the history of roads, the decade encompassing World War I is a watershed. You can see it in the proliferation of the automobile as the personal transportation preference of the average American. You can see it in the increasing mileage of trucks hauling freight. You can see it in one other area as well. In the World War I era, the ancient tradition of deference to localism in road building changed. The Maryland State Roads Commission and the federal government's Bureau of Public Roads were much more than "study and tell about it" agencies. They disbursed money, set standards and supervised construction. They were only one step away from deciding where roads would go and how they would get there.

 In 1917 the SRC took advantage of the opening of its first major bridge project to publicize its good works. The first vehicle to pass over Baltimore's Hanover Street Bridge included not only a delegation of SRC and state dignitaries, but representatives from the press. Top row left to right, Governor Emerson C. Harrington, SRC Chairman Frank H. Zouck, *Star* newspaper reporter Anderson, SRC Chief Engineer Henry G. Shirley, State Treasurer Dennis, *News American* reporter Brattan, Secretary Wilson, Police Officer McLaughlin, *News American* reporter Harman, *Sun* reporter Gibson, SRC Bridge Engineer R. G. Browing, Secretary to the Governor Lockard, SRC Resident Engineer E. H. Wroe.

Henry Ford on the automobile: "When I'm through, everybody will be able to afford one, and about everybody will have one."

Will Rogers on Henry Ford: "It will take a hundred years to tell whether he helped us or hurt us, but he certainly didn't leave us where he found us."

 Left to right, Harvey Firestone, Henry Ford, Thomas Edison, and an unidentified driver take a ride through Hagerstown during one of their well-publicized camping trips.

CHAPTER 3

Good Roads Between the Wars

One would be hard pressed to find two contiguous decades in American history that stand in such stark juxtaposition as the "roaring" 20s and the "hard times" 30s of the 20th century. However, in both boom and bust times, the State Roads Commission financed and supervised the construction of roads at a furious tempo.

Roads were paved from Baltimore to each of the county seats in an attempt to keep pace with motorists' demand.

On June 4, 1924, the ten-millionth Model T Ford automobile was produced. "I will build a motorcar for the great multitude," Ford promised, and the multitude took to the roads. During the decade of the 1920s, the number of automobiles in Maryland increased from 100,000 to more than 300,000.

The State Roads Commission tried to meet the onslaught of motorists with innovative ways to build roads. The district engineers added concrete shoulders two to three feet away from existing asphalt roads, then the roadbeds were expanded out to their new raised shoulders. This cost-saving technique permitted one half of the road to be used, even as the other half was widened with new asphalt or concrete. The resulting resurfaced road was wider, thicker and more durable.

The district engineers painted white lines down the middle of the resurfaced roads, making them safer as well. The "Maryland Shoulder" was widely copied by other states.

Other innovations — like the three-lane highway (the middle lane a passing zone) and the nine-foot wide road (two tires would be on paved road even if the other two weren't) — proved unsafe or shortsighted and were abandoned.

GOVERNOR ALBERT *Ritchie* 1919 - 1935

In 1924 and again in 1932, Albert C. Ritchie (r) campaigned for the presidency of the United States. His states' rights platform may not have won him a national following, but Marylanders liked him enough to elect him their governor four times. Here, Ritchie gets support from Baltimore Mayor Howard W. Jackson.

Governor Albert Ritchie (1919 to 1935) on the relationship between the federal government and the states: "The Federal Government can scarcely be said to 'aid' the states, when all it does is take money from the people of the states and then give it back to them again. Most certainly the federal government does not 'aid' the states, when what it actually does is give back only a part of what it collects from them, and keeps the rest to pay the cost of expensive bureaus maintained for the purpose of giving it back. Back to States' Rights!"

VOTE RIGHT!

Where This sign stands There was once a Toll Gate, For a horse And wAGON. The Toll was 1-½ cents a Mile And for An Auto 2½ cents. The gas tax That The State wants to PUT ON TO PAY BACK The Good road Bonds will Be only ABOUT 3/10 of A cent a mile And The good roads will SAVE More gas Than that

VOTE FOR The BOND ISSUE AND SAVE MONEY

On the Eastern Shore "road gangs" or "crews" traveled in these humble vehicles. The box at the rear of the truck was called a "dog box" after the crates that hunters use to transport their hunting dogs. The boxes were loaded onto trucks and crew members rode inside to job locations.

A vote for a gas tax is a vote for progress! Local residents use an old tollgate as a setting to advertise and advocate for Governor Ritchie's new gas tax, the first to provide dedicated revenue for Maryland roads.

The patrol system of an earlier era was supplemented in the 1920s by the "floating gang." These gangs consisted of a foreman and a crew of six or seven workers. The crews followed behind the patrolman and went over each section of road in their district twice a year to perform major repairs. The vehicle at left from Cumberland, District 6, demonstrates the floating gang's means of transport.

Before his appointment as SRC Chairman, John N. Mackall served as SRC Chief Engineer and is credited with developing the "Maryland Plan" in 1918, a method of widening roads by adding concrete shoulders. This road-building technique was widely copied throughout the United States. Here, a concrete shoulder takes shape alongside the existing Frederick Pike in Howard County.

MAP
OF
MARYLAND
SHOWING
FEDERAL AID SYSTEM IN MARYLAND
AND THE LOCATION OF PORTIONS OF IT IMPROVED
WITH FEDERAL AID
1917 TO 1930 INCLUSIVE
Information furnished by Courtesy of The U. S. Bureau of Public Roads

LEGEND

Roads on Maryland State Road System which are Federal Aid Roads

Location of Projects improved with Federal Aid

U. S. Numbered Highways

Although Maryland already had a primary road system well established by 1915, few of those roads led to other states. When the federal government passed legislation in 1921 asking the states to designate a primary and secondary system, interstate connections became more apparent.

THE *Federal* GOVERNMENT

Although Henry Shirley may have led the charge for a national highway system, his successor as Chief Engineer, John N. Mackall, served a governor with a more state-focused agenda. Appointed Chairman by Governor Albert Ritchie, Mackall concentrated his efforts on expanding Maryland's secondary road system. Mackall served as SRC Chairman and Chief Engineer from 1919 to 1929. He is the only person to have ever held both SRC positions simultaneously.

Adding 3-foot concrete shoulders to many of Maryland's existing U.S. routes allowed the SRC to meet new federal requirements while also dedicating the bulk of its budget to expanding secondary state routes. This photo also features the recently adopted U.S. sign.

35

One innovation in the 20s was overdue – snow removal. Before 1920, only rising temperatures removed snow from Maryland highways. However, the SRC made pioneering tests, documenting that snow and ice removal was more cost-effective than repairing road damage in the spring.

Maryland was among the first states to have a snow-removal policy, but having a policy and actually making roads passable were two different things. Mechanized snow-removal equipment was not in wide use in 1922, the year a blizzard brought over two feet of snow to the mid-Atlantic, crushing the roof of the Knickerbocker Theater in Washington, D.C., killing 98 theater patrons, and paralyzing transportation in Maryland. Opening Maryland's highways took two to four days of labor with hand shovels and horse-drawn plows.

The year 1922 was remembered as the year of the "Knickerbocker Storm," but two other significant events occurred in Maryland road history as well. The first state tax on gasoline was enacted to raise revenue to build and maintain roads, and the SRC used gas tax revenue to build a new road, State Route No. 3.

State Route No. 3 wasn't an upgraded county road or even a repeat of State Route No. 1, a combination of county roads totally funded by the state. State Route No. 3 was a new road where none previously existed. It was long, straight, completely paved and designed to withstand automobile and truck traffic. State Route No.3 opened in 1927 and was named after Robert Crain, a Baltimore lawyer who was the first to propose this superhighway of its day.

Snow Removal

Before the advent of modern snow removal equipment, local farmers put their ingenuity to work and did the work with horse-drawn plows.

When shoveling snow proved an effective way to keep traffic moving during WWI, the SRC decided to make snow removal an integral part of its maintenance program. Formalized snow-removal operations began in 1921. With a lantern hung from its cab, this Western Maryland truck demonstrates preparedness for nighttime as well as daytime duty.

Before 1921, when snow fell, commerce stopped. This delivery car for a wholesale grocer sits abandoned in Garrett County, waiting for the thaw.

Crain Highway's two paved lanes would take one into Southern Maryland. It was an immediate success and soon developed a constituency of merchants who opened businesses along its path.

In 1920, there were 2,000 miles of paved road surface in Maryland. By 1930, at the end of a decade of aggressive road building, an additional 1,200-paved miles of roads were in place. However, little attention was paid to connecting Maryland's paved roads to roads in other states.

No one was more aware of the limitations of the nation's road system than the State Roads Commission's former chief engineer, Henry Shirley. Shirley had a unique perspective. In 1918, he left the SRC to assist in the war effort at the Council of National Defense's Highway Transport Committee. There he gained firsthand experience with the inadequacies of a national highway system built at the whim of local interests. Shirley knew that even a good state road system like Maryland's was built to reflect local needs and subject to local politics. That was by design.

Historically, road building was a local endeavor. Even the milestone Federal Aid Road Act of 1916, which for the first time gave states matching grants to build roads (federal-aid roads), did not tell states where to build the roads, as long as the roads would be used to carry the mail. If the federal government simply turned road-building money over to the states, and worse yet, if the states simply turned it over to the counties, then Shirley concluded, the result would be a highway network "spotted with and not linked by federally-constructed highways."

Crain Highway (MD 3) was the state's first superhighway. It was a new road that ran 32 miles between Anne Arundel and Charles counties. Its primary purpose was to join Southern Maryland farms with Baltimore City ports by a more direct route. Construction began in Upper Marlboro with the dedication of the Crain Highway monument on September 30, 1922. An interesting feature of the new roadway was a traffic circle similar to those found in urban locations such as Washington D.C. The completed highway opened on October 22, 1927.

Robert Crain led the charge to build Maryland's first road where no path had been before and was honored by having the highway bear his name.

Crain Highway

CELEBRATING THE SRC'S *First New* ROAD

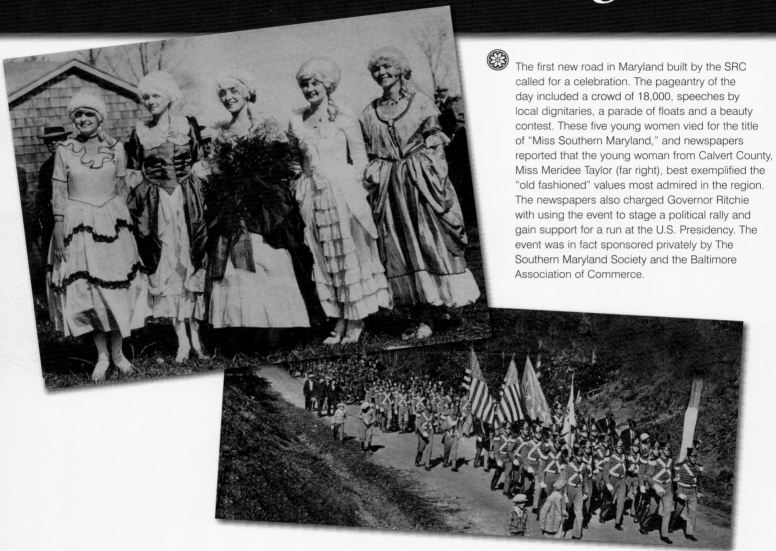

The first new road in Maryland built by the SRC called for a celebration. The pageantry of the day included a crowd of 18,000, speeches by local dignitaries, a parade of floats and a beauty contest. These five young women vied for the title of "Miss Southern Maryland," and newspapers reported that the young woman from Calvert County, Miss Meridee Taylor (far right), best exemplified the "old fashioned" values most admired in the region. The newspapers also charged Governor Ritchie with using the event to stage a political rally and gain support for a run at the U.S. Presidency. The event was in fact sponsored privately by The Southern Maryland Society and the Baltimore Association of Commerce.

Taking advantage of modern machines while recognizing the increased speeds of automobiles, the SRC made an effort to construct its first new highway on a relatively flat terrain with a minimum number of turns. This photo of Crain Highway depicts some of the larger cuts required to keep grades to a minimum.

Today U.S. 301 has absorbed the southern part of MD 3 and the northern part is Interstate 97. All that remains of the original State Route No. 3 is 9.56 miles of commercially-congested highway between Millersville and Bowie. Business MD 3 in Glen Burnie is an orphan, now entirely separated from its parent route.

After President Thomas Jefferson had paid for construction of a National Road across the mountains, one of his successors, James Monroe, turned the road over to the states for maintenance. States such as Maryland promptly erected toll gates to raise the necessary revenue and keep the road in operation. This 1910 photo shows the LaVale toll house after the National Road received its regional name, the Cumberland Pike.

The key concept of Federalism is the delegation of enumerated authority to legislative bodies in ever-larger units of government, from local to state to national. In theory, the closer the political unit is to the people, the greater its claim to do the people's will. In practice, the larger the political unit, the more resources are available to do the will of the people. This conundrum plays out in every issue that works its way through the political food chain. Roads are no exception.

The Constitution of the United States does not list road ownership as an enumerated power of the federal government, but in 1806, President Thomas Jefferson signed legislation authorizing a "national" road from portage on the Potomac to portage on the Ohio River. The legislation required the consent of the states through which the National Road would run — Virginia, Maryland and Pennsylvania — and this "compact" with the states satisfied Jefferson that the road was constitutional.

The precedent of a federally built road on a state-owned right-of-way was never a comfortable fit for Jefferson's party. It was too much like the "elastic" interpretation of the Constitution that Alexander Hamilton and John Marshall articulated.

In 1822, President James Monroe vetoed a bill allowing the federal government to collect tolls on the National Road because it implied a federal right of sovereignty over the road. The logical implication was that if the power of the federal government

extended only to the building of the road, and then only with the states' consent, the completed road should be given to the states. All of the pieces of the original route of the National Road were eventually returned to Virginia, Maryland, Pennsylvania and the new state of Ohio.

If the Jefferson precedent of nationally owned and built roads had not been derailed by Monroe's toll road veto, we would have a very different history of roads in the United States. That didn't happen. When it came to road building in the United States, highways were constructed on the shifting sands of Federalism.

In Maryland, the towns and counties built roads. At first, the state gave free advice. Later it paid for half of the construction of the local roads, and finally it used the power of the purse to make policy and set standards. This is how the State Roads Commission gained control of roads.

If you change the state advice-giver (the Maryland Geological Survey) to the federal government's Office of Road Inquiry, and the state-funding agency (the Maryland State Roads Commission) to the federal government's Bureau of Public Roads, the same dynamic that played out between county and state played out between state and nation in the 1920s. This is how the first national highways since the National Road came into existence.

In 1919, Shirley helped found the Federal Highway Council. The purpose of the council was the promotion of a revolutionary idea — the creation of a nationwide system of federal interstate highways under federal control. Ironically, Shirley became a national roads advocate from a state whose governor was making a career criticizing the incursion of the federal government into state affairs.

That governor was Albert Cabell Ritchie, the longest-serving governor (four terms) in Maryland history. Ritchie supported good roads, but he was suspicious of federal-aid roads that made the states dependent on federal funding. During his administration, the first Maryland gasoline tax was passed in 1922. The gasoline tax was a user-based tax in the tradition of the automobile licensing and registration tax. The federal government would not tap this source of revenue until 10 years after Governor Ritchie did.

Both Shirley and Ritchie passionately believed in good roads, but Shirley said that they should be national roads. Ritchie objected. He had to. Albert Ritchie wanted to be President of the United States.

Ritchie was the country's foremost advocate for the repeal of the 18th Amendment, Prohibition, and twice sought the Democratic Party's nomination as the "wet" alternative to "dry" Republican presidents. Prohibition, Ritchie said, was a "drastic federal infringement" on state and personal rights.

The *Baltimore Sun* cheered him on and lauded Maryland as the "Free State" because the General Assembly refused to pass a state enforcement act for Prohibition. Governor Ritchie couldn't rail against government bureaucrats and endorse a federal highway system with a big new federal bureaucracy to run it.

This SRC pavement demonstration booth graced the floors of the 1925 Southern Exposition in New York City. The exhibit boasted Maryland as "The Pioneer Road Builder of the South and the Best Roaded State of the Union." With recent ventures into snow removal, the SRC could also count "2,500 Miles of Modern Highway Perfectly Maintained Every Day of the Year."

A leader among road-building states during the early 20th century, the SRC turned much of its attention after WWI to road construction and repair in the state's more remote regions. The 1920s would be a boom time for Maryland's secondary routes. Here an SRC maintenance crew demonstrates a "road drag," an early mechanism for grading dirt roads.

U.S. HIGHWAY *Sign* DESIGNS

These early U.S. highway shields helped motorists navigate the streets of Baltimore City before beltways and bypasses became the main routes of interstate travel.

The design of the U.S. highway sign is a shield with three designations: one for the state's name, one for the letters "U.S." and one for the highway number. The American Association of State Highway Officials saw little need for the state name, but the states insisted on it anyway.

Henry Shirley didn't get a system of highways run by the federal government — the roots of federalism were too entangled for that — but those who shared his vision did take a step in the direction of a nationwide highway system with federal highway legislation in the 1920s. In 1921, states were required to use some of their federal-aid money to build roads that were "interstate in character," meaning that the roads connected with another state's roads at the state border.

In 1926, "federal-aid" roads that crossed state borders were identified with a distinctive U.S. Highway "shield" and a common number. With the application of a common logo and number, a national highway system, of a kind, was invented overnight.

Maryland's north/south "interstates" carried the prefix "U.S." and an odd number, those going east/west an even one. U.S. 50 was an "interstate in character" linkage of federal-aid roads that went all the way from Maryland to California. The "0" was a way of noting that this "naught" highway was transcontinental.

The linkage of federal-aid roads from state to state began to look like a national highway system after 1929, when the American Association of State Highway Officials (AASHO) published a manual setting standards for highway signage. An interstate traveler now had uniform signs that pointed the way to his destination and automobile road maps to help plan the trip, even if the roads that took him there were seldom designed as the most efficient routes across the states.

In the 1930s, the federal government's Bureau of Public Roads requested "scientific" surveys of the states' road systems. Maryland's survey revealed on a state level what Henry Shirley knew to be true of all of the states and what he wanted to avoid replicating in a national highway system. There had been lots of paving of local roads and some new state roads built as well, but there were still roads being built that were not state-of-the-art engineering. They had curves that were too sharp, grade crossings with railroad tracks and they led to bridges too narrow for the traffic directed towards them. Most telling of all, as Shirley had predicted for the country as a whole, Maryland roads were a

patchwork of improved highways and not a state highway system.

The dual-lane highway is what the SRC proposed to create a Maryland highway system. Dual-lane highways were state-of-the-art highway engineering and they looked the part. These "show" roads consisted of two lanes of traffic traveling in one direction and two lanes traveling in the opposite direction. Grassy median strips separated the two sets of lanes from each other. Local roads could tie into them and become main arteries of a highway system. If the dual-lane highways met other states' highways at the state border, they were eligible to carry the U.S. highway shield.

There was much to be said for the dual-lane "show" roads of the 1930s. They streaked out from Baltimore going west to Frederick (U.S. 40 west), south to Annapolis (State Route 2, Ritchie Highway) and north to Havre de Grace (Pulaski Highway, U.S. 40 east). They brought a distinctively modern and aesthetic quality to Maryland roads. They were safer than two-lane highways and they allowed for greater speeds.

Truckers proved indispensable to the country during WWI, and their numbers only increased throughout the 20s and 30s. Of continuing concern was the ever-increasing size of their payloads. The statewide planning surveys of the 1930s established checkpoints to determine truck weights and later analyzed what effect those weights had on road surfaces.

Other survey interests ranged from analyzing road-building materials to finding the most efficient routes of travel. Special vehicles were also outfitted to measure road curvature and sight distances.

"Where did you come from?" and "Where are you going?" These were the basic questions asked by survey workers during planning studies. The resulting data would later determine which roads needed improvement. In some cases, the data suggested returning a few state roads to the counties.

Surveys AND Experimentation

During the Depression era 1930s, road construction became a way to keep people employed. Many contracts were let with the stipulation that contractors do the majority of the work using hand labor. Work crew sizes increased and the work week was shortened from 40 to 30 hours. The 1930s were also known as a time for study and experimentation. These workers lay experimental "Specification 6" on a road in Western Maryland.

In the 1930s the federal government's Bureau of Public Roads, the funding agency for Maryland's federal-aid roads, got a New Deal title: the Public Roads Administration (PRA). President Franklin D. Roosevelt (FDR) himself tasked the newest addition to the New Deal's "alphabet soup" of government agencies to propose a transcontinental federal highway system of the type that Henry Shirley and other federal highway visionaries had recommended.

Given the fact that the New Deal had a history of major public works projects, and the Public Works Administration (PWA) was already involved in subsidizing road building in all of the states, good roads proponents were optimistic that the 1930s would yield coast-to-coast federal highways. It didn't happen. Estimates of the cost far exceeded estimates of toll-generated revenue and a plan to sell land in excess of highway needs was called a socialistic scheme. There was one other reason as well: Adolph Hitler.

In the 1930s, Germany constructed the National Motor Road, a transportation milestone touted by the Nazi Party. It was a cross-country system of limited access highways, like those FDR proposed, and like FDR's proposal, fighting the Great Depression was a rationale given for its construction. Creating an American national highway system invited a comparison with the autobahn and gave an invitation to FDR's more strident critics to compare him to Adolph Hitler. After Supreme Court rulings in 1935-36 that the National Recovery Administration and the Agricultural Adjustment Administration exceeded authority delegated to the government in the Constitution, New Dealers were sensitive to being compared to a dictator. A federal Interstate Highway System did not become part of the New Deal.

A meeting of the District Engineers, Maryland State Roads Commission, Baltimore, January 4, 1932.

Seated from left to right: Chief Draftsman Lawrence A. Kahn; District 4 (Towson) Engineer Douglas P. Campbell; Bridge Engineer Walter C. Hopkins; Assistant Chief Engineer Robert M. Reindollar; Chief Engineer Harry D. Williar, Jr.; Chairman G. Clinton Uhl; District 6 (Cumberland) Engineer Leo T. Downey.

Standing from left to right: Maintenance Engineer Frank P. Scrivener; District 3 (Upper Marlboro, western section) Engineer Edward G. Duncan; District 7 (Glen Burnie) Engineer Edward H. Nunn; District 8 (Upper Marlboro, eastern section) Engineer Joseph Chaney; District 2 (Chestertown) Engineer Ralph Townsend; District 1 (Salisbury) Engineer Patrick A. Morison; Secretary Lamar H. Steuart; Chief Auditor William A. Codd; Purchasing Agent Richard F. Goeing; Field Engineer Charles B. Bryant; District 5 (Frederick) Engineer Thomas M. Linthicum; and Engineer of Surveys Austin F. Shure.

THE *Severn River* BRIDGE

Built between two world wars, the Severn River Bridge and Governor Ritchie Highway were considered state-of-the-art bridge and highway construction. The Severn River Bridge is shown here under construction in 1924 with workers in the foreground and the previous timber bridge to the left. A new bascule structure will soon fill the center span.

 As the SRC began to build dualized roadways, many Marylanders became concerned with the aesthetics of ever-expanding lanes. Maryland garden clubs, led predominantly by women, sought to introduce landscaping and beautification measures. Taking a tip from these clubs, the SRC planted new trees in median strips. Then one day while working on Ritchie highway, SRC inspector and later the agency's photographer, William T. "Scoops" Claude, made the recommendation to leave the old ones in place. This photo shows Governor Ritchie Highway north of Arnold.

SRC legend has it that Governor Albert C. Ritchie laid a ruler on a map to indicate his preferred route for MD 2, thus accounting for the straightness of the state's first "show road." Whether or not Marylanders take this legend as truth, the method of highway design before WWII tended to keep things simple. The sweeping curves of modern highways that help drivers combat highway hypnosis did not come into wide use until after WWII. After Ritchie's death in 1936, MD 2 was dedicated as the Governor Ritchie Highway in his honor.

For the first time, the SRC was building a statewide system of state-of-the-art highways and bridges. There is a lesson to be learned by studying the history of two of these Maryland projects completed between the world wars — a road on land and a road over water — and what happened when the state of the art passed them by.

The Severn River is the gateway to Annapolis, the state capital, from the east. In 1924, the SRC built an 1,850-foot long bridge over the Severn River and celebrated the accomplishment with fanfare unlike that for any other road-building project. Then in 1934, the SRC built one of its new dual-lane "show" roads to connect the Severn River Bridge to points north and south. The bridge was simply called the Severn River Bridge, but the highway became the Governor Ritchie Highway.

You could drive from Baltimore on Ritchie Highway's dual lanes and pass another car without the need to estimate the distance of a car coming in the opposite direction. As you approached Annapolis, old growth trees became part of the landscape. They had been carefully preserved by the SRC. At the Severn River, a bridge appeared, seeming to float on the water. Together, bridge and highway blended into the natural topography of river and land.

The Severn River Bridge's 22-foot roadway, flanked by two sidewalks, and Ritchie Highway's dual lanes separated by a landscaped median strip, spoke to the spirit of 1930s modernity that characterized the best of bridge and road building between the world wars.

Both the Severn River Bridge and Ritchie Highway were state-of-the-art roadwork in their day. However, their day did not last long.

The appearance of the Severn River Bridge floating on the river was due to the fact that it was only 15 feet above the water. The

Severn River Bridge was a two-lane drawbridge. In 1924, no one thought that a drawbridge was an intolerable access barrier to Annapolis. One could get out of the automobile and walk the sidewalks to see the passing boats. A drawbridge was a diversion that added to the pleasure of driving.

The pleasure diminished over a 20-year period of growth in automobile ownership. After World War II, when the bridge opened its double-leaf bascules to let boats pass, traffic backed up so far that you couldn't see the river. Traffic patterns after World War II were not kind to Ritchie Highway either. In 1934, people lived close to where they worked. Ritchie Highway was designed to move people quickly and safely. No one thought that it would produce an exodus from Baltimore or that commerce and traffic lights would follow the highway's dual lanes into the country. Ritchie Highway became the "Main Street" in a contiguous row of unincorporated bedroom communities from Baltimore to Annapolis.

Even after 1953, when a new bridge arched upstream over the Severn River, letting boats and cars pass without interfering with each other, the "old" Severn River Bridge remained an object of affection for many Annapolitans, who used it as a backdoor to Annapolis. However, Ritchie Highway's nickname, "Chrome City," was a reference to the many car dealerships on its northern end, and was less a sign of affection than irritation on the part of commuters driving to work in Baltimore.

A lesson learned in road and bridge building between the world wars is that state-of-the-art is not a static condition. There is another lesson to be learned as well. Building highways is a physical science — roads built to withstand the demands of what travels on them. But it's also a social science, anticipating the social consequences of what highways will become.

Building small bridges like the South River Bridge in the early 1930s prepared SRC forces for an expansive bridge program that would be initiated in 1938. Here, workers stand over a swing span mechanism similar to that used on the larger Choptank River Bridge of 1934.

 Abel Wolman's influence on public works projects in Maryland, nationally and internationally is unparalleled. A civil engineer (pictured on page 47) who made his mark primarily in the area of water quality and water distribution, he also contributed significantly to Maryland transportation planning. Wolman served as the first director of the Maryland State Planning Commission (now the Maryland Department of Planning) and in the 1930s was tasked with directing a study of the Maryland road system. Also during those years, Wolman headed the blue-ribbon panel that helped develop Maryland's Primary Bridge Program.

CHAPTER 4

Good Roads and the World War II Era

After three decades of state funding for roads, the Maryland State Planning Commission confirmed what the State Roads Commission had known since the days of Henry Shirley. Maryland had overbuilt secondary roads at the expense of a statewide highway system. A report was issued under the chairmanship of Dr. Abel Wolman of Johns Hopkins University.

Abel Wolman

In 1935, it didn't require a stretch of the imagination to see how this had happened, but it required political courage to point it out. In 1904, when Maryland began giving state aid for road building, 90 percent of all roads in Maryland were unpaved. Paving any unpaved road was visible progress and when the paved roads went to county seats, it looked like planning was taking care of itself. The Wolman Report pointed out that widening and paving roads to county seats wasn't producing a statewide highway system.

The Wolman Report provided the rationale to loosen the tethers of localism and create a state highway system built around a backbone of dual-lane highways. However, there was a challenge that wasn't political — three rivers and the Chesapeake Bay. These ancient waterways severed the links in the Maryland highway system.

The bridge-building record of the SRC in the 1930s was impressive in terms of numbers of bridges — 250 were built in that decade — and in terms of innovative bridge design. Perhaps the most impressive bridge of that era was the longest one, the Choptank River Bridge on the Eastern Shore.

The Choptank River Bridge was built with a swing span instead of drawbridge leaves. It was less expensive and more reliable than a drawbridge opening. In 1935, President Franklin D. Roosevelt attended the bridge dedication and the presidential yacht, Sequoia, was the first vessel to pass through when the swing span opened.

Named the Emerson C. Harrington Bridge after Maryland's wartime governor, the Choptank River Bridge remained in service for 52 years. When a new bridge was built in 1987 and dedicated to State Senator Frederick C. Malkus Jr., the center steel trusses (three stationary, one center swing span) of the Harrington Bridge were removed. The two remaining approach spans, one on each shore of the Choptank River, were converted into fishing piers.

Spectators take in the recently completed 1.75-mile span that would cut 15 miles off a trip from Easton to Cambridge. An estimated 3,000 spectators turned out for the Harrington Bridge opening.

THE *Choptank Bridge* CELEBRATION

Governor Harry Nice presides over the ribbon cutting that would join residents of Dorchester and Talbot counties, October 26, 1935. The $1,400,000 bridge was the first Public Works Administration project in Maryland and part of President Roosevelt's New Deal program.

To celebrate the bridge opening, President Roosevelt docked his boat at Long Wharf at the end of Cambridge's Main Street. The President's brief speech included a thank you to his close friend, Maryland Senator George L. Radcliffe, who first suggested the importance of building such a bridge 15 years earlier. The Eastern Shore also seemed to agree with Roosevelt. "If I have a chance," he said, "I am coming over here again to visit with you during my term."

Trusses for the Choptank River Bridge were constructed at Sparrows Point and floated down the Chesapeake on barges, good practice for the Bay Bridge that would come 15 years later.

Surveys and construction on the Choptank River Bridge began during the winter. Pete Cooper, a recent engineering graduate of the University of Maryland, had the duty of inspecting the concrete. One pour lasted until midnight and after covering the forms with tarps, he stayed up to check the heaters and see to a proper curing.

Project Engineer on the Choptank River Bridge, Elmer White (center), measured the length of the triangulation system for the bridge by walking on Choptank ice floes and pulling a boat behind him. White trained many SRC bridge inspectors who went on to complete major Maryland road projects, including William Kahl, later of RK&K Engineers. After the Choptank, White supervised construction of the Susquehanna River Bridge. He is shown here during construction of the Marshy Hope Creek Bridge in 1932 flanked by Superintendent Percy Slaughter and President Ted Bonsel of Bonsel & Brook contractors. District 1 Engineer Pat Morison stands to the far right.

When a new bridge spanned the Choptank River in 1987, the original bridge was converted into a fishing pier. Shortly after this photo was taken, the steel truss center spans were removed.

The Chesapeake-Potomac hurricane rolls through Ocean City, creating an inlet and Assateaque Island.

Philip "Pete" Cooper entered SRC service in 1931 and served 20 years with the agency. After getting his start on the Marshy Hope Creek Bridge, Cooper inspected construction on the Choptank River Bridge, the Cambridge Creek Bridge and the Sinepuxent Bay Bridge to name a few.

PHILIP *Pete* COOPER

When the Chesapeake-Potomac hurricane created the Ocean City Inlet and Assateague Island in 1933, Cooper worked seven days and nights to restore the wooden bridge. He used telephone poles and guardrail wire to create a temporary fix, and Ocean City tourists were still able to enjoy their Labor Day holidays that year.

Taking time out to serve in WWII, Cooper returned stateside to become special assistant to William "Buck" Childs II in Baltimore. Childs appointed him the first SRC research engineer, and Cooper performed the earliest investigations into asphalt at a time when most Maryland highways were still constructed primarily of concrete and tarmac.

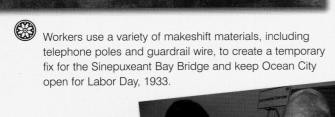

Workers use a variety of makeshift materials, including telephone poles and guardrail wire, to create a temporary fix for the Sinepuxeant Bay Bridge and keep Ocean City open for Labor Day, 1933.

In 1950, Cooper was Project Manager on the U.S. 50 Severn River Bridge when he got an offer to become the Public Works Director for his hometown city of Salisbury. Although retired from that position since 1978, Cooper remains active. At 98, he attended an SHA open design forum, contributing ideas for a new Sinepuxent Bay Bridge, one that will serve the demands of modern beach traffic.

MDOT's Heather Murphy and Pete Cooper at a design forum.

THE *Primary Bridge* PLAN

In the New Deal 1930s, spectacular public works were the order of the day. In this heady environment, one might have been tempted to think the unthinkable. The SRC could build bridges anywhere and do it with technological innovations that made it affordable.

In 1937, Maryland's Republican governor, Harry W. Nice, took a page out of FDR's game plan for fighting the Great Depression and convinced the General Assembly to give the SRC an unprecedented challenge: build bridges across the Susquehanna River, a fresh water source of the Chesapeake Bay; the Potomac River, boundary between Maryland and Virginia; and the Chesapeake Bay, divider of Maryland into Eastern and Western shores. A bridge to Baltimore over the Patapsco River was called for as well. It became a tunnel under the Port of Baltimore.

The plan to bring these extraordinary projects to fruition in the 1940s was known as the Primary Bridge Plan. It was "primary" in terms of creating a highway system by connecting links over Maryland's primary waterways. It also was as complex in implementation as it was bold in concept. Financing would have to be a state/federal partnership and Congress would have to approve any plan since it had regulatory approval over navigable waterways. The Maryland General Assembly added two new ideas of its own: The Primary Bridge Plan would be supported by revenue from tolls and a citizens' committee would be established with veto power over SRC actions.

In spite of the magnitude of the undertaking, the first bridge in the Primary Bridge Plan opened in the summer of 1940. Crossing the Susquehanna River was a daring first choice, given the SRC's previous experiences.

For 200 years, ferries had crossed the Susquehanna between Havre de Grace and Perryville in northeastern Maryland. A railroad bridge was built in 1873. In 1910, a private group of investors bought the Pennsylvania Railroad Bridge and converted it into a toll bridge for automobiles.

The conversion was flawed from its inception, because the roadway was only 13 feet wide. Two automobiles going in opposite directions could pass, but a slight miscalculation by either driver would result in a sideswiping accident. The solution was to slow automobile speeds to a snail's pace.

After Maryland's experience with military trucks in World War I, it was obvious that the old railroad bridge would not be able to handle truck traffic. In 1923, the obsolete bridge was offered for sale. SRC engineers knew the bridge's shortcomings, but they thought they had a solution. They were wrong.

Maryland acquired the old railroad bridge and added an additional lane, but not as a parallel construction. A deck was built over the bridge, creating dual roadways, one on top of the other. When complete in 1926, the project was considered a success. However, that assessment underestimated Maryland roads' old nemesis, the truck. They grew wider and they grew taller, too.

The vertical clearance between the two bridge decks was only 12.5 feet. In the 1930s, many trucks could only cross the lower bridge deck by deflating their tires to avoid being wedged in. This was visible evidence of poor design. What

was conceived as an engineering feat was openly criticized as a waste of money. In addition, it was reported that the owners of the bridge had made a million-dollar profit on their investment, the largest piece coming from the sale of the obsolete structure to the state. In derision, the bridge was called the "Gold Mine" bridge.

The SRC admitted the futility of putting more money into the "Gold Mine" bridge and a new upstream crossing of the Susquehanna became the first of the Primary Bridge projects. The new Susquehanna Bridge was built of steel and from a distance it looked like a

railroad viaduct, perhaps not surprising since it was designed by the J.E. Greiner Company, specialists in railroad bridges. However, the new bridge was very different from a railroad viaduct. It had four lanes and a width of 46 feet. Named the Thomas J. Hatem Memorial Bridge in 1986, it is now the oldest toll facility operating in Maryland.

The second bridge in the Primary Bridge Plan spanned the Potomac River and was completed a few months after the Susquehanna Bridge. Unlike the Susquehanna Bridge, there was no history of failed bridge building on the Potomac. In fact, the Potomac Bridge was

THE "GOLD MINE" BRIDGE . . .

 Investing in this railroad bridge over the Susquehanna proved a stroke of genius for a few lucky Maryland businessmen. Once they began charging tolls, 60 cents or greater depending on cargo weight, the money poured in and helped to earn the bridge a new name, "The Gold Mine Bridge." The SRC purchased the bridge and added its second deck, shown here in 1926. However, the bridge soon became obsolete and the label "Gold Mine" became a term of derision.

 A trail of automobiles heading south along U.S. 40 emerges from the lower deck of the "Gold Mine Bridge." Two other autos, moving north, climb toward the bridge's upper deck.

The "Gold Mine Bridge" had a number of interesting features. On its lower deck, truck drivers were sometimes known to deflate their tires in order to maintain proper clearances between their trailers and the bridge structure above. Two-way traffic was also tight as demonstrated in this 1925 photo, with the wise driver moving slowly so as to avoid a scrape.

the first bridge over the Potomac south of Washington, D.C. Crain Highway was extended from Mattawoman in northern Charles County to an existing ferry site, which became the northern end of the bridge. The southern end of the Potomac Bridge is in Virginia, giving an interstate ambience to the groundbreaking ceremonies, which President Franklin D. Roosevelt attended.

The Japanese attack on Pearl Harbor on December 7, 1941, changed everything. The bridge-building schedule in the Maryland Primary Bridge Plan was not an exception. From 1942 until 1946, the priorities of the federal government were building military access roads to war plants and military installations. Everything else was put on hold.

Sometimes the federal government's wartime priorities and civilian priorities were the same. For example, U.S. 40's proximity to Aberdeen Proving Ground made it a high priority for upgrades that served both civilian and military needs. However, most of the road-building funds spent under the Defense Highway Act of 1941 were not high priority projects from a civilian point of view.

Crossing the Chesapeake Bay and the Patapsco River had to wait for the end of World War II. This would give the Primary Bridge Plan the contours of a doughnut - a hole surrounded by the crossings of Maryland's major waterways, if the plan was to be continued at all.

Times changed from the beginning of World War II to the end of it. Before the war, there was monetary deflation and big construction projects helped fight the Great Depression by putting more money into the economy. After the war, wage and price controls were lifted and costs rose. There was no longer a consensus that the government needed to stimulate the economy.

...THE *Susquehanna River* BRIDGE

 The Susquehanna River Bridge between Havre de Grace and Perryville supplied the missing link to U.S. 40, a dual-lane highway from Baltimore. The old "Gold Mine" bridge was disassembled and used for scrap metal during World War II. In 1986, the bridge was renamed the Thomas J. Hatem Memorial Bridge to honor the prominent Harford County resident.

. . . THE *Potomac River* BRIDGE

 Opened in December 1940, the Potomac River Bridge is of steel cantilevered construction, which means the roadway extends beyond the bridge's piers. It is only a two-lane bridge, but it spans 1.7 miles across the Potomac River. Because the Potomac River is navigable below Washington, D.C., there is 135-foot clearance above the shipping channel. The bridge was completed at a cost of $5,500,000 and the original toll price was set at 75 cents for passenger vehicles.

Governor Harry W. Nice initiated the Maryland Primary Bridge Program of 1938. In 1967, the Potomac River Bridge was renamed the Governor Harry W. Nice Memorial Bridge in his honor.

THE TIMES OF WILLIAM "Buck" Childs

Highway visionaries came and went during the long career of William "Buck" Childs, but from the days of Henry Shirley to the dawn of the interstate era, he was the glue that connected their visions.

Buck Childs began his career at the SRC in 1912 as one of Henry Shirley's motorcycle-riding District Engineers. Unlike most of his colleagues, he was the graduate of a university (Cornell) engineering program. This helped him make the transition from those seat-of-the-pants road-building days to modern planning and budget projections.

After stints as the district engineer at Salisbury and then Frederick, Childs became manager of the state planning survey, director of the transportation study of the Baltimore metropolitan area and the first head of the SRC traffic division. In 1941, he prepared a comprehensive planning document that the Baltimore *Evening Sun* called "the most exact analysis of the State's highways, as they are and as they should be, that has ever been made."

Governor William Preston Lane, Jr. made road building a top priority of his administration, and the SRC picked Buck Childs as the chief engineer who could make the limited access concept — the heart of Lane's Five-Year Program — work. Escalating construction costs caused by the Korean War doomed Lane's five-year goals, but Childs was able to show that the limited access principle was the way to control the kind of commercial over-development that had strangled Governor Ritchie's "show roads." Lane's successor, Governor Theodore McKeldin, adopted the limited access principle and Buck Childs wrote it into McKeldin's Twelve-Year Program. But the 68-year-old Childs resigned as chief engineer so that a younger man could see it to completion.

Short of being named SRC Chairman, William "Buck" Childs (1886-1966, seen at far left) worked at the SRC for 36 years and held just about every prominent position that an SRC employee could hold: Road and Bridge Inspector, District Engineer in two districts, Bridge Consultant, Director of the Traffic Division, and Chief of the Highway Planning Surveys. After being chosen Chief Engineer under SRC Chairman Robert M. Reindollar in 1947, Childs retained that position under Chairman Russell H. McCain until his retirement in 1953. Here, he explains future road plans to Governor McKeldin while Chairman McCain (center) looks on.

"Mr. Maryland Roads" left the SRC after a career that spanned the four decades between Henry Ford's "Model T" and Dwight Eisenhower's Interstate Highway System. However, Buck Childs didn't stop making contributions to Maryland's roads. In 1957, Childs chaired a blue-ribbon committee that warned the General Assembly that for both aesthetic and safety reasons, legislation was needed to control the proliferation of highway billboards. He was determined that the new limited-access expressways weren't going to become the "Billboard Boulevards" of his early days as a district engineer. The federal government came to the same conclusion eight years later, when Congress enacted the Highway Beautification Act of 1965.

55

Crossing the Chesapeake Bay by bridge was a very old dream in Maryland, but few would have thought that a politician from the western end of the state dreamed it as much as those who lived near the bay. William Preston Lane, Jr. was from Hagerstown, the Attorney General of Maryland under Governor Ritchie and a direct descendant of several pioneer families that settled the mountains of Western Maryland. He was elected governor in 1946.

It would have been politically expedient to walk away from the Chesapeake Bay Bridge. The Bay Bridge was a priority from another time and even Lane conceded there were other pressing state needs, like public education and the state mental health system. Nevertheless, Governor Lane urged the General Assembly to continue the primary bridge goal of crossing the Chesapeake Bay.

The J. E. Greiner Company said there were two ways to do that, one from Baltimore and one from Annapolis. The Annapolis route was chosen because it was shorter, albeit over deeper water, and more centrally located between both ends of Maryland's Eastern Shore. It was nearer to Washington, D.C. as well.

In 1947, Governor Lane asked the General Assembly for a bond issue to build the Chesapeake Bay Bridge. The bonds would be repaid by tolls. This was the same type of user-fee employed in building the Susquehanna and Potomac bridges. However, that was not all that Lane wanted. He also wanted to build a new type of highway. Lane's highways were to be "expressways," dual lane highways with median dividers, but they also were limited access roads with grade separations at all intersections. They had

one other characteristic: they were expensive. The Expressway Act of 1947 increased the gasoline tax and vehicle licensing fees. It was the heart of Governor Lane's "Five-Year Program," Maryland's attempt to jump start highway building after the neglect of the war years.

Governor Lane asked the General Assembly for a 2-cent sales tax on the dollar, the first state sales tax in Maryland history. Although revenue from the sales tax was not specifically dedicated to roads and bridges, with every purchase it was a constant reminder that Governor Lane was a "big spender." The Chesapeake Bay Bridge was a big spender's project.

Work on building a bridge from Sandy Point, outside of Annapolis, to Kent Island on the other side of the bay, began in 1949. The engineering challenges were unique. The Bay Bridge would have to be more than four miles long, the longest continuously over-water structure in the world, and it would have to rise above the Baltimore shipping channel, one of the busiest port access routes in the United States.

Joining Maryland's two shores with a ribbon of concrete highway utilized two types of bridge design, one crossing the shipping channel and one leading to it from both sides of the bay. The heart of the Bay Bridge is a 1,600-foot long suspension span. It has massive concrete piers that support two 354-foot main towers strung with 14-inch thick steel cables.

The suspension span is a magnificent sight in itself, as it towers 186 feet above the main navigation channel of the Chesapeake Bay. However, there is more to the Bay Bridge than this Golden Gate-

Project Engineer Bruce Herman of J. E. Greiner Engineering and Governor William Preston Lane, Jr. discuss plans for the Chesapeake Bay Bridge during one of the Governor's site visits. After 30 years of planning, Governor Lane saw to it that Maryland finally got its bridge across the bay. When later asked why the bridge only had two lanes, one in each direction, the former governor would respond that if he had chosen to build more than two, Maryland would have never gotten the bridge at all. The final cost for the structure was a whopping $45 million, about eight times more expensive than the preceding Potomac or Susquehanna projects.

like center span. From both sides of the bay, a gentle arch of 123 steel spans of cantilever trusses, simple trusses, plate girders and beams tie the suspension span to the land.

The Chesapeake Bay Bridge opened in 1952 at a cost of $45 million, and was commonly acknowledged as one of the great engineering and aesthetic accomplishments of the 20th century.

In 1950, Maryland voters, experiencing rapid inflation and trying to balance household budgets, defeated Governor Lane's bid for re-election by the largest margin in Maryland history at that time.

Iron workers from New York were brought in to erect the bay structure. A number of them included American Indians from the Kahnawake tribe of southwest Quebec, Canada. The Kahnawake had an established tradition that dated back to the 1880s of working on high structures. They were noted for their daring on skyscrapers such as the Empire State Building in New York.

THE *Chesapeake Bay* BRIDGE

While surveyors work from the platform beyond, these men finish off a pier cap before the steel superstructure can be set in place. Photographs indicate that African-American men did much of the concrete finishing work on the structure.

These steel workers demonstrate the common method of working from a wooden platform, which was in turn suspended from the superstructure by ropes. While the first Bay Bridge was constructed with hot rivets, shown in this photo, the second Bay Bridge used all welded and bolted connections.

These men assemble a narrow footwalk between the bridge's main towers about 350 feet above bay waters. From this platform, 61 pre-stressed wire ropes were strung from tower to tower, forming a single 14" diameter suspension cable.

A new sign ushers in a new way of life for Marylanders on Eastern and Western shores alike.

The finished bridge with its elegant curve, which was required in order to accommodate a central shipping lane channel under its suspension span.

One of the final runs of the SRC ferry boat, shown here in 1951. The Bay Bridge rises beyond.

Theodore Roosevelt McKeldin, the winner of the 1950 gubernatorial election, inherited Lane's bridge and road-building initiatives without the burden of being labeled a New Deal "big spender." McKeldin was a Republican. Like his namesake, Theodore Roosevelt, he was not your average politician. McKeldin brought unbridled energy to politics. He seemed to lose as many elections as he won — he lost races to be Mayor of Baltimore and Governor of Maryland before he won those offices — but he always ran again.

Thanks to his penchant for showmanship, McKeldin's name would become as prominent in highway building after World War II as Albert Ritchie's had been before the war. However, there was a difference. Ritchie wanted to minimize the role of the federal government in road building.

McKeldin wanted to expand it. As Mayor of Baltimore, McKeldin had worked with the federal government in building an airport. The airport was named Friendship International after a Quaker meetinghouse that once occupied the land. It was an appropriate name for another reason. To McKeldin, the federal government was an important friend in public works projects.

Governor McKeldin was a self-made man, the son of a Baltimore stonecutter who later became a policeman. To help support his family, young McKeldin worked as an office boy after completing grammar school and took night courses to complete his high school and college education. He enrolled in a Dale Carnegie course at the YMCA, liked public speaking and became a politician. Dedicating public projects was McKeldin's forte and he delighted in

being the state's number one highway booster.

McKeldin, often climbing on top of bulldozers to the delight of the press, opened more than 100 stretches of highway, but his signature project was a tunnel. The Primary Bridge Plan called for crossing the Patapsco River, and thereby connecting both sides of the Baltimore Harbor, by bridge. In 1938, the Greiner Company estimated that a bridge would be a third less expensive than a tunnel. However, in the 1950s, the SRC produced estimates projecting that a cost-effective tunnel supported by tolls was feasible.

A tunnel crossing Baltimore Harbor would still be more expensive than a bridge, but using the open-trench method of construction could narrow the cost differential. The open-trench method called for dredging a trench in the harbor bottom, then sinking pre-fabricated tunnel sections to the bottom of the trench and joining them underwater. The tunnel also was less of a hazard to air and shipping over Baltimore's busy port. There was one other reason: Governor McKeldin liked the tunnel. The Bay Bridge was his predecessor's accomplishment and it was named after William Preston Lane, Jr., as well. No Maryland governor had built a tunnel under a port.

The biggest environmental challenge in building a tunnel under water is removing noxious automobile fumes. The Holland Tunnel under the Hudson River in New York solved this problem with a fan-driven ventilation system. Ole Singstad, the world-renowned expert who had perfected the Holland Tunnel's ventilation system, was hired as a consulting engineer and construction began in January 1955, at a crossing between Canton and Fairfield. Governor McKeldin attended the sinking of the first tunnel section, and posed for pictures perched on a winch set to do the job, only to be sent home by Singstad who was not satisfied with the trench grade until the ninth try.

THE BALTIMORE *Harbor Tunnel*

Twenty-one twin-tube steel sections, each approximately 300 feet long and 69 feet wide, served as the core for the underwater portion of the Baltimore Harbor Tunnel. The sections were fabricated at three different shipyards, launched like ships and towed to the tunnel site.

From the motorist's perspective, the tunnel is a two-lane highway with ceramic tiles on its sidewalls. The space over the ceiling, like the area under the roadway, was left hollow and used for ventilation ducts. The ventilating system is similar to that originally developed for the Holland Tunnel in 1920 by Ole Singstad. When it was completed, the Baltimore Harbor Tunnel was the longest trench-type tunnel ever built and the fifth longest of all the world's underwater vehicular tunnels.

60

In 1957, the Baltimore Harbor Tunnel opened. It consists of 21 twin-tube sections, each 300 feet long. It was the first tunnel built by the open-trench method to have four traffic lanes and it was an immediate success. However, the Baltimore Harbor Tunnel's success was due to more than just being a tunnel, even a state-of-the-art one. The approaches to the tunnel are 16 miles of expressway, limited access dual-lane highways. The tunnel and its expressway removed 40 percent of truck traffic from Baltimore's streets and neighborhoods. The "Baltimore Bottleneck," the last major obstacle to north/south traffic on the East Coast, was gone.

The opening of the Baltimore Harbor Tunnel marked the completion of the Primary Bridge Plan. For 20 years, from the General Assembly's approval of the concept in 1937 to the completion of the last project in 1957, the Primary Bridge Plan engaged the engineering talents of the best minds in the public and private sectors. The result was astonishing; all of the projects are first-class accomplishments and the Chesapeake Bay Bridge and Baltimore Harbor Tunnel are engineering marvels of world-class stature.

 The Patapsco River Bridge? Had decision makers chosen a bridge over a tunnel, Marylanders might still be crossing the Patapsco from above rather than below. This drawing from Maryland's Primary Bridge Program of 1938 proposed an alternate structure in case the necessary funding could not be found.

 Governor Theodore McKeldin provided sensational dedications for both the Chesapeake Bay Bridge, opening July 30, 1952, and the Baltimore Harbor Tunnel, opening November 29, 1957. Here, the governor prepares to take his first pass through the newly-finished Harbor Tunnel in his trademark white Cadillac convertible. McKeldin's enthusiasm for landmark highway projects was recognized in 2005, when the Baltimore Beltway (I-695) was officially dedicated in his memory.

This sign most certainly raised the spirits of East Coast travelers who dreaded entering traffic jams along the busy streets of Baltimore City. The new tunnel cut driving time through Baltimore from 50 minutes to 20, eliminated an estimated 51 traffic signals, and added one more link in the dream of completing an East Coast superhighway.

Tying the country together.

Before the interstate program, Maryland began constructing important expressways such as U.S. 111. Today, we know this road as I-83. This photo indicates one of the important byproducts of building highways — new development. To the right can be seen office buildings rising in Hunt Valley. A 23.5-mile section of the Baltimore-Harrisburg Expressway opened on June 15, 1956 only days before President Eisenhower signed the interstate bill.

The seeds of Dwight Eisenhower's vision of an Interstate Highway System can be traced to 1919, when the 28-year-old Lieutenant Colonel left his peace-time posting at Fort Meade and joined a column of 81 Army vehicles for a transcontinental trip from Washington, D.C. to San Francisco.

If any national organization understood the importance of a functioning road system, it was the U.S. Army. After facing the challenges of military transport during WWI, the Army became an avid promoter of good roads. The cartoon (above) records the lighter side of the First Transcontinental Motor Convoy. "The old convoy had started me thinking about good, two-lane highways…," Eisenhower recorded in his memoirs.

CHAPTER 5

The Age of Eisenhower

Dwight D. Eisenhower is seldom mentioned in conversations about the greatest presidents of the United States. In fact, within the context of the presidents who preceded him (Franklin D. Roosevelt and Harry Truman) and the ones who followed him (John F. Kennedy and Lyndon Johnson), the Eisenhower 50s seems a respite between larger-than-life personalities.

Dwight D. Eisenhower

However, if American history is seen in its roads, then the Eisenhower years stand above all others. What Thomas Jefferson tentatively began with the National Road and what Franklin D. Roosevelt only ruminated about, Eisenhower accomplished. President Eisenhower created the Interstate Highway System.

In the 1950s, Eisenhower made the times and the times made Eisenhower. He was a victorious general from World War II, the president who ended the war in Korea and the man Americans trusted to keep the country safe from Communism. Eisenhower didn't ask for much — no "Square Deal" or "New Deal" or "Fair Deal" — so, when he asked for something, people listened.

At the Governors' Conference in upstate New York in 1954, Vice President Richard Nixon informed the governors that President Eisenhower had a "Grand Plan" for a national highway system. The governors had heard the pitch for a national highway system for the last 20 years, but most of them still did the math the way Albert Ritchie had. If you add up what the citizens of your state pay to the federal government in gas taxes, and federal excise taxes on automobiles, trucks, tires, oils and grease, and then subtract what your state gets back in federal-aid highway funds, it's a negative cash flow. Equally perplexing to the governors listening to Vice President Nixon's speech was the total absence of a strategy to pay for the "Grand Plan."

The convoy outside of Rockville, Maryland. Eisenhower missed the convoy's departure from the Ellipse in Washington, but joined up with it at the Frederick Fair Grounds later that evening, July 7, 1919.

A covered bridge over Tom's Creek in Emmitsburg, similar to the replica pictured here, was one of the first obstacles the convoy encountered. It was too low to accommodate military vehicles, causing a long detour. This proved an omen of what lay ahead. Many bridges were not as fortunate; the convoy destroyed 88 of them on its way to the West Coast.

The covered bridge that had survived the convoy in 1919 was not around in 2006 when SHA helped celebrate the interstate program's 50th anniversary. Instead a scaled-down replica of the old covered bridge at Tom's Creek provided the setting. Government and private sponsors from across the nation recreated the historic journey, and this time in reverse, from San Francisco to Washington D.C. Ethanol-powered cars provided the primary means of transport.

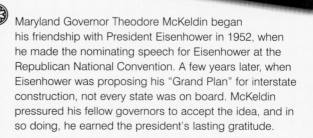

Maryland Governor Theodore McKeldin began his friendship with President Eisenhower in 1952, when he made the nominating speech for Eisenhower at the Republican National Convention. A few years later, when Eisenhower was proposing his "Grand Plan" for interstate construction, not every state was on board. McKeldin pressured his fellow governors to accept the idea, and in so doing, he earned the president's lasting gratitude.

However, the governors did hear something that day that they had not heard before. Nixon said that President Eisenhower wanted a national highway system because it would meet the demands of national defense, "should an atomic war come."

The linkage of federal highways with an atomic war was a potent combination. The image of nuclear bombs falling on American cities, with only national highways to evacuate their residents, was palpable. The "Grand Plan" had something else going for it besides Cold War hysteria: it had friends in Maryland.

At the Republican National Convention in Chicago in 1952, Governor Theodore McKeldin nominated Dwight Eisenhower for president. He urged Eisenhower to make highways a part of his campaign, and although Eisenhower had a more important campaign issue, ending the Korean War, he did tell the Hearst newspapers that the nation's highway system "presents an appalling problem of waste, danger, and death." Eisenhower knew what good highways looked like. His troops used the autobahn during the invasion of Germany.

In 1951, Governor McKeldin came into office on a platform that called for a review of Governor William Preston Lane's highway-building policies. To most Marylanders, that sounded like a fiscal conservative, and fiscal conservatism is what the voters wanted after World War II. They elected McKeldin governor, but McKeldin's secret was that when it came to building roads, he planned to do more of the same.

In 1953, the year before Eisenhower's announcement of a "Grand Plan" for federal highways, McKeldin presented the Maryland General Assembly with an

ambitious road-building agenda that carried the Expressway Act of 1947, 12 years into the future. Using the existing federal-aid formula, the federal government would pay for 50 percent of McKeldin's "Twelve-Year Plan." However, the package carried an estimated price tag of a sobering $568 million, and that estimate, at a time of rapid inflation, was based on 1947-52 cost figures.

As Mayor of Baltimore, McKeldin worked with the federal government in building Friendship International Airport. He had none of the reservations about federal-state partnerships that Albert Ritchie had, but McKeldin knew that raising taxes had led to Governor Lane's defeat, and he did not want to suffer the same fate.

Eisenhower's "Grand Plan" was political cover for the highway-building dreams of a state governor. Marylanders would have to pay more in taxes for expressways, but if they were federal taxes, there wouldn't be a political price to pay at the state level. Governor McKeldin became a "Grand Plan" supporter. Maryland's advice to the other state governors was now the complete opposite of what it had been in the 1930s. McKeldin said that governors who opposed the "Grand Plan" were suffering from a case of "buck fever."

In addition to Governor McKeldin, it would take another Marylander's contribution to make the "Grand Plan" a reality. He was a Democrat, not a Republican, but that's what made Representative George H. Fallon's support invaluable. The Democrats controlled the House of Representatives in 1956 and all appropriation bills must originate in the House. That meant that Fallon, as the chairman of the Subcommittee on Roads of the House Public Works Committee, would have a

formative role in shaping the "Grand Plan." Fallon could relate to the "Grand Plan" because of his work with a road-building partnership from the 1940s, the Baltimore-Washington Parkway.

The "parkway" was a term and a concept from a different era. Parkways were roads built for the experience of riding through a park. They were popular entryways to European capitals and Pierre Charles L'Enfant's original design of the United States Capital envisioned a grand parkway in the European tradition.

The federal government had joined the parkway movement in the 1920s with the Mount Vernon Memorial Parkway. The Blue Ridge Parkway and Skyline Drive were New Deal parkways built to create jobs and stimulate the economy, and the Norris Freeway was a parkway addition of the Tennessee Valley Authority.

In 1942, construction began on the "Capital Gateway" parkway. Five years later, Governor Lane included an expressway to parallel U.S. 1 in the Maryland Expressway Act of 1947. Representative Fallon saw the common elements — controlled access, grassy medians and above-grade intersections — that characterized both types of roads. If Maryland's new expressway met the parkway, the result would be an expressway through a park.

Like the "Grand Plan," this was a new way of looking at a federal-state road-building partnership. There was another portentous aspect to Fallon's involvement. He used a national defense rationale. The new highway would link Fort Meade with the nation's capital and one of its most important port cities, Baltimore.

 Baltimore County Planner and Landscape Architect Malcolm H. Dill is credited with envisioning the Baltimore Beltway. At its completion, Dill remarked, "It ties the whole county closer together." Looking west, this photo (left) shows the Charles Street intersection in the foreground and the Baltimore-Harrisburg interchange to the right. Extending I-83 along the Jones Falls would occur a few years later.

The Baltimore Beltway began as a Baltimore County government initiative in the late 1940s. The county had high hopes, but determined that it would never have enough money to complete it. When Governor McKeldin incorporated the belt road into his 12-year program in 1953, the State Roads Commission took over development. The photo below shows the new alignment as it runs to Joppa Road in 1955. The Baltimore-Harrisburg Expressway Interchange can be seen beyond.

Expressways AND Freeways

The look of the Interstate Highway System owes much to highways built in Maryland before 1956. The reason is Governor William Preston Lane's highway program. Under the Expressway Act of 1947, the General Assembly authorized construction of "expressways."

Expressways, like the "show roads" of Albert Ritchie's day, were defined as two or more lanes moving in opposite directions that were separated by median dividers. However, by 1947, the history of show roads, like MD 2 (Ritchie Highway), exposed their weakness.

What distinguished the expressways envisioned under Maryland's Expressway Act of 1947 from the dual-lane show roads of the 1930s were grade separations, bridges at intersections and limited access. The Act of 1947 was a model for federal interstate highway standards. The term "freeway" was used to emphasize that interstate highways were free from private entrances and at-grade crossings with other roads.

The standards for interstate highway construction required moving earth on an unprecedented scale. Maximum slopes in mountainous regions were limited to 6 percent. The need for heavier equipment required that diesel engines replace the steam and gas power of the past.

In 1953, Governor Theodore McKeldin unveiled his ambitious 12-Year Roads Program at a cost of $568 million. Three years later, when Eisenhower signed the Interstate Act on June 29, 1956, the Governor made his case for taking advantage of the new 90/10 ratio of federal-to-state funding. The revised cost for the program was estimated at $885 million. Maryland's portion of the interstate mileage would be 353.6 miles.

Land being cleared in preparation for the construction of the Baltimore Beltway in May 1961, a familiar sight during the age of interstate construction. This land was located near the current Cromwell Bridge Road interchange.

67

The Baltimore-Washington Parkway was opened in 1952, with the high speed limits, dual lanes and limited access characteristics of an expressway. It was not a leap of the imagination for Fallon to play the national defense card again in 1956, by arguing that highways like the Baltimore-Washington Parkway could take city residents out of harm's way as easily as they could take them for a ride in the country.

What emerged from Congress as the Federal-Aid Highway Act of 1956 owes much to two contributions from Congressman Fallon's subcommittee — one in the form of a rejection and the other in the form of an endorsement. Fallon rejected both the idea of paying for interstates by issuing bonds, which had been recommended by a blue-ribbon panel headed by Ike's World War II subordinate, General Lucius D. Clay, and by collecting tolls, as several states had done. The second contribution was to keep alive the rationale that Vice President Nixon had given to the governors. Fallon labeled the highways envisioned in his bill the "National System of Interstate and Defense Highways."

The Federal-Aid Highway Act of 1956 passed Congress as a continuation of the 1916 precedent of federal-aid funds being given to states to build highways, but this was not a Woodrow Wilson era highway act. The federal government set design and construction standards, thus creating uniform highways that traveled to destinations planned by the federal government.

The piece of the "Grand Plan" that Nixon had not mentioned was added by George Fallon's committee. It was a way to pay for

them, called the "Highway Trust Fund." The Highway Trust Fund received its revenues from federal taxes on gas and diesel fuel and from user fees and excise taxes. The sellers of taxed commodities collected the taxes, which were paid to the Internal Revenue Service and deposited into the fund. However, what created a favorable impression among the states was a change in the traditional federal-state funding formula from 50/50 to 90/10, with the federal government's share being 90 percent.

There is an irony associated with the creation of the Highway Trust Fund. Its most vociferous opponents would be the greatest beneficiaries of the interstates. Trucking, gasoline, oil, tire and auto manufacturers assumed that they would be charged excise taxes to keep the trust fund solvent; they were right, but the explosion in motoring that was stimulated by interstates did not have a consumer backlash. Federal excise taxes were passed on to the motoring public without reducing demand for the products that carried them. For the moment at least, the economic truism that increased costs reduce consumption was stood on its head.

The 1956 Highway Act was based on a new rationale and a new funding formula, and it envisioned the construction of 41,000 miles of interstate highways to be built between 1956 and 1972. At that pace, it would be the largest road-building effort in world history.

The new federal-aid funding formula delighted good roads governors like Theodore McKeldin. The state tab for building expressways dropped from 50 percent to 10 percent for the 350 miles

of interstates planned for Maryland. The Baltimore-Harrisburg Expressway and the Washington National Pike from Frederick to near Chevy Chase were expressways already half completed in 1956, and the remainder qualified for the 90 percent funding formula. The former became I-83 and the latter, I-70S (now I-270). New interstates paralleled parts of older U.S. routes, like U.S. 40 and U.S. 1, and essentially replaced them for purposes of interstate travel.

The interstates connected all parts of the continental United States and circled many of its large cities with "beltways" that routed traffic around congested urban centers. Building circumferential highways was seldom done (the first was constructed in Boston in 1951) because acquiring property in densely populated areas was expensive and time-consuming. However, the new federal-aid funding formula made beltways affordable, and it ignited an explosion in beltway construction.

Even before the interstate highways, Governor McKeldin wanted to construct a circumferential highway around Baltimore. His rationale wasn't to bypass Baltimore, but to create an expressway as a wheel around the city that connected its suburban-fringe communities to each other, and all of them to the city core via highway spokes. There was a compelling reason to do it — the Servicemen's Readjustment Act of 1944 (better known as the G.I. Bill). The G.I. Bill provided low interest, zero down-payment home loans for the returning veterans of World War II. Veterans and their families could move out of urban apartments to the city fringe and beyond, if there were roads to take them.

The Baltimore Beltway (right) opened officially on July 1, 1962 as 32.8 miles from Ritchie Highway to Pulaski Highway, linked by the Baltimore Harbor Tunnel. The two 12-foot concrete lanes in each direction cost $68,457,686. As part of its orientation to beltway driving, the SRC offered Marylanders booklets with map inserts as shown at right. Newspapers, however, reported that many Marylanders found the circular road disorienting. Drivers found themselves literally traveling in a circle, confused about how or where to get off the road. Residents who lived close to the road reported frequent knocks at their doors from travelers who had experienced breakdowns or ran out of gas.

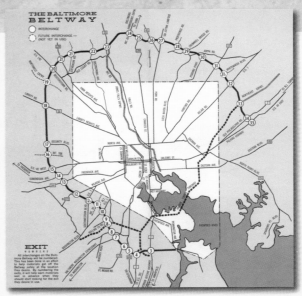

State Roads Chairman John Funk (far right, in photo at left) returns from a flyover inspection of the Baltimore Beltway. When construction of the beltway began in the 1950s, Funk was Director of Public Works in Baltimore County. After Governor Tawes appointed him State Roads Chairman in 1959, Funk oversaw the project to completion. Standing to his right is Enoch Chaney, SRC District Engineer for District 4.

THE *Baltimore* BELTWAY

 After its opening, the Baltimore Beltway's traffic reached near-capacity in 18 months and soon needed to be expanded from four to six lanes. SHA construction inspector John Schene, who began working at the SRC in 1958 recalls, "I'd worked on the original beltway, but by 1962 we were back adding lanes between Wilkens Avenue and Route 40." Schene says that the original four concrete lanes soon became six, but afterwards additional lanes were added as asphalt, and the entire road was given an asphalt resurfacing.

 In 1977, the construction of the Francis Scott Key Bridge expanded the eastern portion of the Beltway to 53 miles by crossing Baltimore's Outer Harbor. The bridge is 1.6 miles long and has steel truss cantilevered-arch main spans with four traffic lanes.

The Francis Scott Key Bridge and its highway extension were not part of the original interstate plan, and received the MD 695 designation, but it's the part of the I-695 Beltway that's favored by trucks carrying restricted materials or that are too large to use in the harbor tunnels. It cost $60.3 million.

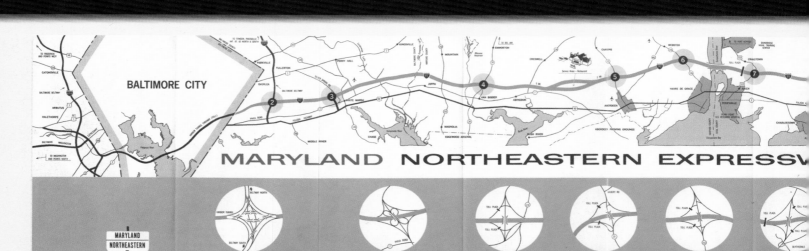

BALTIMORE CITY

MARYLAND NORTHEASTERN EXPRESSW

MARYLAND NORTHEASTERN EXP. 95

BALTIMORE BELTWAY INTERCHANGE EXIT 2 ➋
Connections with expressway loop around the city of Baltimore, linking principal suburban communities plus radial routes such as Jones Falls Expressway, Baltimore-Harrisburg Expressway, Route 40 West and others. This is Beltway Exit 33.

THE WHITE MARSH INTERCHANGE EXIT 3 ➌
Southern terminal of the toll portion of the expressway. Southbound traffic keeps straight for Baltimore and suburban communities via Beltway; Baltimore Harbor Tunnel, Washington and points south. Leave here for Middle River, Chase and White Marsh area.

ROUTE 24 INTERCHANGE EXIT 4 ➍
Leave here for Edgewood Arsenal, Emmorton, Bel Air and other central Harford County points.

ROUTE 22 INTERCHANGE EXIT 5 ➎
Leave here for Aberdeen (including U.S. Army Proving Grounds), Churchville and central Harford County points.

ROUTE 155 INTERCHANGE EXIT 6 ➏
Leave here for Havre de Grace, Level Road, Susquehanna State Park and northern Harford County points.

ROUTE 222 INTERC
Leave here for Port Dep Bainbridge, Veterans H Point, and points on Susquehanna River.

 This brochure for the Northeastern Expressway (I-95) details its 42.4-mile route of which seven miles were toll-free. A state bond was issued for $74 million but the final cost was estimated at $104 million. This included the $10 million Millard E. Tydings Memorial Bridge. The brochure also features the newly constructed Maryland House, a welcome center for out-of-state visitors.

In 1953, plans were drawn to connect disparate population clusters on Baltimore's edge — Linthicum, Catonsville, Pikesville, Towson, Parkville, Essex and Dundalk — via a beltway, but little actual work was done. Then came the Highway Act of 1956. Construction entered the fast track when the federal-state funding formula changed from 50/50 to 90/10.

The Baltimore Beltway was completed in 1962. As the first beltway constructed under the 1956 Highway Act, it was a model that many large cities followed, including Washington, D.C. The Baltimore Beltway (I-695) was a witness to what beltways do — bypass cities and, if connected to arterial highways, facilitate the relocation of city residents to the suburbs.

At a time when his critics said a beltway was "a road to nowhere" because it was a circle, Governor McKeldin believed that people would use it. He was right about that. Beltways became the most heavily used part of Maryland's interstate highway system. In 2005, the Baltimore Beltway was dedicated to Governor Theodore McKeldin.

What highway planners had not anticipated is that beltways and interstate highways compress miles into a different standard of measurement — time. Moving to the cadence of time, minutes in transit instead of miles traveled becomes the relevant statistic to the suburban commuter. By the standard of the clock, rural areas became enviable locations for bedroom communities.

There was another area in which time had an impact upon would-be users of interstate highways. Timing was everything under the rules of engagement of the 1956 Highway Act. The 90 percent federal funds had a shelf life, so the State Roads Commission initiated a "Go Program" to ensure that all of Maryland's interstate highways were underway before federal funding expired. This included a beltway around Washington, D.C., I-70 from Baltimore to Washington County in western Maryland, and the Northeastern Expressway. The Northeastern Expressway was the first part of I-95, the interstate that runs from Florida to Maine. President John F. Kennedy attended the ribbon cutting, the only time a president has attended the opening of an interstate highway.

MARYLAND'S *Northeastern* EXPRESSWAY, I-95

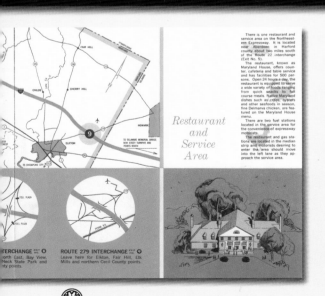

 When Governor Tawes came to office in 1959, he determined that the 12-year construction program was behind schedule and ordered the SRC to begin his five-year "Go Program." The "Go Program" lived up to its name. Construction for the 42-mile Northeastern Expressway (I-95 north of Baltimore) began on March 22, 1962, and was finished by November 1963.

Pictured left at the opening of the Northeastern Expressway, left to right, Delaware Governor Elbert N. Carvel, President John F. Kennedy and Maryland Governor J. Millard Tawes. Behind Kennedy and Tawes, left to right, former Governor Theodore McKeldin, Robert Moses and Congressman George H. Fallon look on.

The picture was taken on November 14, 1963. The following week, President Kennedy was assassinated. The Maryland portion of the interstate from Baltimore to the Delaware line was renamed the John F. Kennedy Memorial Highway in his memory. On the one-year anniversary of President Kennedy's assassination, surprised motorists received a rose from the Kennedy Highway toll collectors in honor of the slain president.

OPENING *Interstate 95*

 When I-95 opened in Maryland, the recent passage of Maryland's public accommodations law dictated that the new highway and its adjoining Maryland House would be open to all. Sensing an opportunity for further change, civil rights demonstrators appeared at the I-95 event and called for a more comprehensive end to the legacy of segregation. One year later, President Lyndon Johnson signed the Civil Rights Act of 1964, making public accommodations throughout the state and the nation open to all.

CALL BOX

When it opened, the Capital Beltway featured call boxes that would allow stranded motorists to summon police, firemen, ambulances or servicemen in the event of a breakdown. This publicity photo features a woman demonstrating proper use of a call box as well as her distress. Unfortunately, SRC maintenance crews often found the boxes vandalized and almost impossible to maintain. The boxes were eventually removed for maintenance and safety reasons.

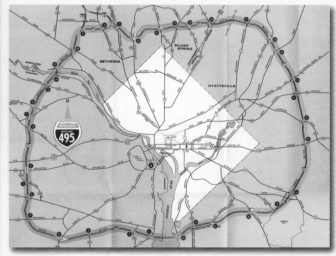

First envisioned by the Maryland National Capital Park and Planning Commission in 1952, the Capital Beltway was originally called the "Washington Circumferential Highway," but this name later changed to the "Capitol Beltway." When someone pointed out that the word "Capitol" might only refer to the seat of Congress, the spelling was changed to what we know today. The 43.2-mile Maryland section of the Capital Beltway cost $115 million and opened on August 17, 1964.

The Pooks Hill interchange, showing the intersection of the Capital Beltway with I-270. The new I-270 alignment can be seen winding northwest.

President Eisenhower presented the state with a gift in 1954 when he signed Public Law 83-704. This law created an important link in Maryland's evolving freeway system, the Woodrow Wilson Bridge. While the original bridge opened on December 28, 1961 at a cost of $14 million, the new Woodrow Wilson Bridge, actually twin drawspans, opened in 2008 and cost 2.4 billion, including interchanges.

Ribbon-cutting ceremony at the dedication of the Woodrow Wilson Bridge, December 28, 1961. Front from left, Woodrow Wilson's son-in-law Francis B. Sayers Sr., Secretary of Commerce Luther H. Hodges, and Rep. Joel Broyhill (R-Va.).

It would take Marylanders almost 35 years to complete a limited access highway that would parallel the old National Road and take them to the farthest western reaches of the state. In the meantime, progress on the interstate portion of I-70 was made throughout the 1960s. Here, an SRC paint-striping crew adds the finishing touches to a portion of recently completed highway.

A new 53.5-mile section of I-70 opened on September 28, 1968. First row left to right: SRC Commissioner Walter Bogley, State Comptroller Louis Goldstein, U.S. Congressman Charles "Mac" Mathias, Frederick Mayor John A. Derr, and State Roads Chairman-Director Jerome Wolff.

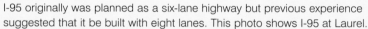

I-95 originally was planned as a six-lane highway but previous experience suggested that it be built with eight lanes. This photo shows I-95 at Laurel.

Maryland officials preview I-95 between the Baltimore and Capital beltways, which opened July 1, 1971. Left to right: Secretary of State of Maryland Blair Lee, III, State Roads Chairman-Director David Fisher, SRC Chief Engineer Walter Woodford, and District 4 Engineer M. Slade Caltrider.

OTHER *Interstate* CONNECTIONS

Sometimes referred to as the gateway to Western Maryland, this photo shows the construction of the 250-foot long, 80-foot high steel arch bridge in Frederick County. The bridge design was suggested by the Federal Highway Administration because of the scenic location atop Braddock Mountain. It was completed in 1972 and carries Ridge Road over I-70.

In 1957, the Bureau of Public Roads (BPR), which had moved to the Federal Commerce Department, reported that interstate planning and construction were "going on at a furious pace throughout the nation." Obviously, Maryland was not the only state to see a good road-building deal when it came along. Some pundits were more critical than the BPR. They said state highway officials had "90-itis" because the federal government was picking up 90 percent of the cost of their highways.

Expanding the workforce and opening regional SRC laboratories for testing local construction materials and soils facilitated the furious pace of interstate highway construction in Maryland. However, private contractors carried out most of the new work. Using consultants in bridge and highway work, like the J.E. Greiner Company, was a key ingredient of The Primary Bridge Program, but the extent of the Interstate Highway System greatly increased their numbers. In some ways, the SRC became a training ground for consultants. Three of the most successful were Wilson T. Ballard, Ezra Whitman and William R. Kahl. These men were former SRC engineers who went on to found highly successful consulting companies that are still in business today.

In terms of mileage, Maryland was not in the same league with large landmass states, but its contribution to the interstate system was large. Maryland provided an Eisenhower loyalist and key interstate highway booster among the governors, in Theodore McKeldin. Representative George Fallon's leadership position in the House of Representatives was critical to the 90/10 funding formula that made a massive highway-building program palatable to the states. Another Maryland contribution was its history with expressways. The

Engineering Heritage

Ezra Whitman

Wilson Ballard

Herschel Allen

William Kahl

The close relationship between former SRC engineers and private firms that they founded, or in which they became senior partners, can be seen in the office of The President of the Maryland Section of the American Society of Civil Engineers. Former presidents with SRC employment in their background include Ezra Whitman (Whitman, Requardt & Associates) from 1921 – 1923, Wilson Ballard (The Wilson T. Ballard Company) in 1932, Herschel Allen (a partner in Greiner Engineering, now a part of URS) in 1937, and William Kahl (Rummel, Klepper and Kahl) in 1954. Ezra Whitman also served as the national president of the American Society of Civil Engineers in 1943.

Maryland Expressway Act of 1947 helped influence what interstate highways would look like, and the Baltimore-Washington Parkway demonstrated that the aesthetics of the parkway movement could be combined with the practical engineering of the expressway.

The country learned from Maryland's engagement with highways and the SRC learned something too. In 1958, Congress created a "Bonus Program," a 1/2-percent increase in the federal share of interstate construction costs, to states that took measures to control outdoor advertising along the interstate system.

Maryland was the first state to join the "Bonus Program." The billboard clutter of Washington Boulevard and its U.S. 1 permutation didn't happen to the Maryland Interstate Highway system.

In Maryland and in the United States, the history of roads exists before and after Dwight Eisenhower. Before him, there were the under-funded and poorly planned U.S. federal-aid national highways built upon the rationale of carrying the mail. After him, there was a self-funding and user-based financing system for building freeways deemed vital to national defense.

By the end of President Eisenhower's second term in 1960, the Interstate Highway System was 25 percent complete. In 1961, Congress raised gas and other excise taxes to complete the system. Although the Interstate Highway System has long since met its original goals, it keeps growing (currently over 47,000 miles). The American Society of Civil Engineers included the Interstate Highway System as one of the "Seven Wonders of the United States." In 1990, the name of the interstate system was officially changed to the "Dwight D. Eisenhower System of Interstate and Defense Highways."

THE "I" Ways

SRC Assistant Traffic Engineer George W. Cassell shows off his prize-winning design for the interstate highway shield. Cassell's design represented Maryland in a national competition sponsored by the Bureau of Public Roads. The design we know today was chosen, but Cassell had the right color scheme. The border line around his map was red, and the letters and numerals were blue on a white background.

In 1957, the Bureau of Public Roads adopted route markers and a numbering system that was developed by AASHO for interstate highways. The interstate system shield is similar to the U.S. Route shield but in bold red, white and blue colors it carries the word "interstate," the state name and the highway number. As with U.S. Route numbers, highways running north and south are assigned odd numbers and those running east and west, even numbers.

The prefix "I" and one or two numbers is the common designation of an interstate highway. In Maryland, there is no single-digit interstate highway. There are, however, beltways and spurs, which are three-digit interstates. Beltways are circumferential highways; they carry three numbers with the first digit being even and the last two designating a major interstate connection. Spurs are interstate highways that have deviated from their parent's route and do not return. They are given three-digit numbers with the first one being odd and the last two designating their parent. For example, I-95 is a 1,927-mile-long north/south interstate highway. It intersects with the 36-mile long Baltimore Beltway, which is numbered I-695, and I-95 has a spur, I-195, which travels five miles to the Baltimore/Washington International Thurgood Marshall Airport (formerly Friendship International Airport).

Healthier living in the cities...

Toll Roads and Free Roads described the ills of the aging American city in stark terms. To Fairbank, (pictured on page 79) it seemed logical that these areas of decay would provide fertile ground for new urban freeways. As a resident of Baltimore, he used his home city to illustrate his ideas.

 Baltimore's Herbert Sinclair Fairbank's career at the Federal Bureau of Public Roads spans the early development of federal-aid roads. His contributions to two pioneering reports from the 1930s and 1940s, *Toll Roads and Free Roads* and *Interregional Highways*, articulated a vision of an Interstate Highway System and provided an analysis of its consequences. Fairbank's expertise was in providing data for policy-makers, but he also brought a gift for anticipating future needs and projecting the consequences of building highways that others did not foresee.

In recognition of Fairbank's use of research to plan highways and his contributions to designing the Interstate Highway System, he was the first recipient of the Association of American State Highway Officials' "MacDonald Award." The research laboratory at Langley, Virginia, now known as the "Turner-Fairbank Research Center," carries his name.

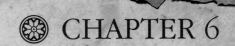

CHAPTER 6

Highways in the City

Bypassing cities is what most Americans believed interstates were supposed to do. Even President Eisenhower is said to have been surprised when he learned that Highway Trust Fund money could be used for building expressways in cities. What was an afterthought to Eisenhower had an interesting history.

Herbert Sinclair Fairbank

At the New York World's Fair of 1939, urban designer Norman Bel Geddes created a model of an urban expressway for the General Motors "Futurama" exhibit. In Bel Geddes' model city, residents busily went about their lives and conducted business while cars moved above them on elevated highways with parkway aesthetics. The projected date of construction was the 1960s, the very time that highway engineers were called upon to take the interstates into the cities.

The "Futurama" predicted "healthier living" in cities with highways in the sky. It had the aura of modernity, but it was closer to science fiction than reality. However, there was a more credible voice speaking of the transformational potential of expressways. His name was Herbert S. Fairbank, and he saw highways as nothing less than the savior of the cities, the agent of a new urbanism.

Fairbank lived in Baltimore and commuted each day to his job in Washington, D.C. In the 1930s and 1940s, his job was Director of Research at the Bureau of Public Roads (BPR).

79

What Fairbank saw firsthand in Baltimore was confirmed by the daily statistics that crossed his desk. American cities were in decay. Fairbank developed a model to explain the phenomenon.

Fairbank's model began with the central business district and data to show that it was becoming "cramped, crowded, and depreciated." Beyond the business district there was evolving a mixed-use area of businesses and residences, which he called "slums," with poor living conditions. An even larger area of depreciated residential property surrounded the slums. This he called the "blighted area." Housing that was more desirable was found at the city's outskirts. When people moved from the blighted area to the city's edge, their former residences were absorbed into the slums.

This scenario was "fraught with great economic difficulties," Fairbank concluded, because the outward movement of city residents would result in a deteriorating property tax base. With reduced taxes, city services would shrink and businesses would be forced to follow the outward exodus.

In Fairbank's analysis, cars were a destabilizing influence on cities, but he hypothesized that this didn't have to be the case if highways were designed to prevent it. The Fairbank concept was to use highways to solve the very problem that cars had exacerbated. The key components in his thinking were two circumferential highways connected by arterial roads. He described the combination of two circumferential highways as a wheel with a rim (the

outside beltway) and a hub (a smaller beltway around the central business district) connected to each other by spokes (arterial expressways). The rim would provide a bypass for travelers to other destinations and the hub, via its expressway spokes, would efficiently move city-bound traffic to local streets where there would be parking garages and access to trains and buses.

Fairbank envisioned the hub around the central business district remaking cities into desirable places to live as well as shop and work. His report from 1941, *Interregional Highways*, has a distinctly modern tone in its emphasis on building highways that were sensitive to the existing urban fabric. He was prophetic in his recognition that urban

MAKING *Plans for Baltimore*

Public works maverick Robert Moses of New York was one of the first to develop plans for a high-speed expressway through Baltimore City. In 1944, Moses presented the plan for a cross-town Franklin Expressway running along the city's Orleans Street and Franklin-Mulberry streets. As part of the scheme, high-density housing (left) would border the expressway, eliminating what Moses described as slum areas (right). Nearly 20 years after this proposal, Moses would attend the opening of the Northeastern Expressway (see photo in Chapter 5).

expressways should not be left to highway builders alone.

The idea of using expressways to reverse urban decay was bold and unprecedented, but in the 1960s, when beltways started circling American cities, the types of planning agencies that might have brought a different urban perspective to the table did not exist. Also, highway planners felt that they were under rigid timelines for accessing federal funds, and they had no track record or experience with building expressways in cities, much less with experiments in social engineering. Consequently, the interstate spurs planned for the central business district in Baltimore didn't promise anything other than to keep the city relevant by making it accessible.

Highway engineers brought the golden rule of building interstates into Baltimore: build the most direct route to your objective at the least possible expense. In American cities, the most direct route to the central business district, at the least expense, goes through slums. Urban mayors applauded that logic because it left wealthier residences and their contributions to the city's property tax rolls untouched. However, what made sense to highway engineers and city mayors made no sense to the less affluent residents whose homes were purchased to build the interstate spurs, especially when they didn't have affordable housing alternatives. Urban slum families, many of whom were minorities who did not own cars, charged that urban interstates were "white men's roads through black men's homes."

The expressways that moved into American cities seemed gargantuan in size from the perspective of the neighborhoods they penetrated. An average right of way of 250 feet would take out an entire city block, and when the highways rose above the skyline on elevated concrete pillars, they cast dark shadows in their wake. When they dropped to ground level, they became blurs of fast-moving cars. When expressways were depressed below ground level to make cars less visible, the engines' roar reverberated against concrete walls.

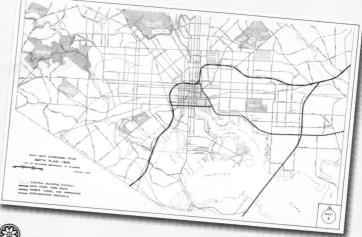

At center, Nathan L. Smith, SRC Chief Engineer between 1935 and 1938 and later Baltimore City Director of Public Works. Smith is shown here at the Cambridge Creek Bridge during his tenure as SRC Chief Engineer. On the left is District 1 Engineer Pat Morison; on the right, Gordon Whiting of Whiting Turner Construction.

After being presented with the Moses plan, Mayor Theodore R. McKeldin drew upon more local expertise. He asked his Public Works Director Nathan L. Smith to develop an inner-city freeway system in 1945. Smith developed an inner-ring freeway that would serve as a template for city planners for the next 30 years.

While the SRC maintained the right to condemn properties for expressway construction throughout the state of Maryland, under home rule in Baltimore City, that right belonged to the Mayor and City Council. City politicians, taking their cue from planners, saw urban expressways as a way to revitalize the inner city. One politician who ushered through numerous urban renewal plans for his beloved Baltimore was City Councilman (1955 – 1967), Council President (1967 – 1971), Mayor (1971 – 1987), and Maryland Governor (1987 – 1995) William Donald Schaefer. This photo shows 5th District Councilman Schaefer in 1957 (far right).

History in the Making...

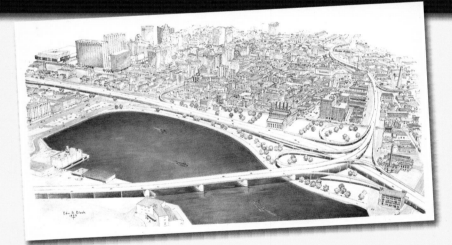

Progress on the 10-D plan was moving along in the early 1960s when city road builders had managed to bring I-83 toward the harbor. Future connections between I-83 and interstates I-70 and I-95 would prove more difficult.

Many alternates had come and gone by the time the Baltimore Planning Commission settled on what was to be called the 10-D plan. Approved by city legislators in 1962, it shows I-70 passing along the north side of the Inner Harbor where later the Inner Harbor Pavilion, World Trade Center, and Baltimore Aquarium took root. Crossing the harbor is I-95, with plans to continue east through Fells Point. I-83 can be seen much as it is today, stretching north through the city.

Theodore R. McKeldin was Mayor of Baltimore and Thomas Ward (center) was 2nd District Councilman. A proponent of architectural preservation, Ward was the lone council voice against the 10-D plan, single-handedly delaying expressway construction in Baltimore for a time by making sure that other council members closely abided by council protocol. Ward was also the primary author of the bill that began Baltimore's Commission for Historic and Architectural Preservation (CHAP). Here, Ward confers with members of the Baltimore Heritage Society, Mrs. James Biays Young and Mr. Clare Davis, February 1969.

PAGE B 6 — THE EVENING SUN, BALTIMO

Expressway Condemnation Passes But Court Suit Is Threatened

By Horace Ayres

A poster advertising the first Fells Point Fun Festival.

When voted out of office, Councilman Ward joined forces with Lucretia Fisher (far left) to begin the Society for the Preservation of Federal Hill, Montgomery Street and Fells Point. Their purpose was to raise awareness of Baltimore's historic structures and stop expressway construction within the city. The City Council had already condemned houses in Fells Point by the time Fisher and other hopeful preservationists began buying them up with the intent of restoring them.

"Fun in Fells Point." To raise money for the expressway fight, the Society for the Preservation of Federal Hill, Montgomery Street and Fells Point began the Fells Point Fun Festival. In the meantime, one Fells Point resident, Robert L. Eney, working with the Maryland Historical Trust and a group of local volunteers, took advantage of a newly-created Federal law to document historic structures. This put Fells Point on the National Register of Historic Places in April 1969, a status that would later make constructing a highway through the area close to impossible.

FELLS POINT FUN FESTIVAL

IN THE SQUARE AT THE FOOT OF BROADWAY

Festival Headquarters
819 S. Broadway, Baltimore, Md. 21231 Tel.: 732-5363

SUNDAY, OCTOBER 8, 1967 · 1 P.M.-6

· RAIN DATE: OCTOBER 15, 1 P.M.-6

ART SHOW · DANCES · MUSIC · FOOD
FLEA MARKET · CLOWNS · RIDES

SPONSORED BY THE SOCIETY FOR THE PRESERVATION OF FEDERAL HILL, MONTGOMERY ST., AND FELLS POINT

Urban expressways divided neighborhoods and they displaced families. Community activists in San Francisco, Boston and New Orleans wanted to stop the expressways, even if it meant stopping them in mid-construction.

Baltimore was in the middle of the urban "road wars." The City of Baltimore maintained jurisdiction over planning decisions within city limits, but because federal highway funds had to pass through a State agency, the Interstate Division for Baltimore City was created as a combined city-state agency to build expressways in the city. It was made up of some of the best and brightest of the Baltimore Planning Commission and the State Roads Commission (SRC).

The plan to bring arterial highways from the beltway into the central business district called for 23 miles of expressway into Baltimore from an I-83 spur from the north, an I-70 spur from the west and an I-95 spur from the south and northeast, meeting in a massive central business district interchange located on the waterfront with a bridge over the Inner Harbor.

Public protest and lawsuits resulted. In Rosemont, a predominantly African-American community, and in Fells Point, the home to many lower and middle-class families with immigrant roots, community opposition was intense. More than 30 community groups, both multi-racial and multi-ethnic, combined to oppose the interstate spurs that would bisect their neighborhoods.

URBAN EXPRESSWAY *Battles* CONTINUE

BALTIMORE INTERSTATE HIGHWAY SYSTEM 3-A

 Community opposition to the 10-D plan caused city leaders to take a fresh approach to freeway planning. They appointed a Design Concept Team to take a second look and gained additional funding from the Federal Highway Administration. Led by the Interstate Division of Baltimore, the Concept Team included noted architects, planners, engineers, economists and social workers gathered from throughout the nation. When the Design Concept Team unveiled the new 3-A plan, city and federal approval came in 1969. Community leaders, however, remained dissatisfied.

Community groups used new federal laws that protected historic buildings (the National Historic Preservation Act of 1966), the environment (the National Environmental Policy Act of 1969 and Clean Air Act of 1970) and especially section 4(f) of the Department of Transportation Act of 1966, which provided protection for publicly owned parks, recreation areas, historic sites, wildlife and/or waterfowl refuges from conversion to transportation use. Even the landmark Civil Rights Act of 1964 was invoked.

A circuit court judge found section 4(f) violations in the plans for an I-70 spur through Leakin Park, and political protests forced the abandonment of the I-83 route across Bolton Hill and the I-95 route over Baltimore's Harbor into Fells Point. A prominent leader in the "Battle of Baltimore" was a fiery community activist named Barbara Mikulski. She parlayed her success in opposing the urban highway plan into a seat on the Baltimore City Council and then a career in the House of Representatives and the United States Senate.

The Baltimore City Council included several road fighters and they were of sufficient force to stop condemning properties. In effect, Baltimore's citizens were saying that they would pass on the opportunity to have a confluence of expressway spurs in the central business district, preferring to preserve the unique historic flavor of their many ethnic neighborhoods, historically significant buildings and public parks.

 Between 1967 and 1971, Mayor Thomas D'Alesandro, III (left, holding shovel) and City Council President William Donald Schaefer (far right) found themselves in the heat of expressway battles. Here D'Alesandro and Schaefer break ground for one of the city's many urban renewal projects. The man at center is unidentified.

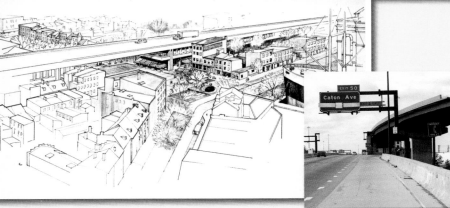

 Once known as "The Ramp to Nowhere," this stub ramp along I-95 reminded Baltimoreans of the interstate that might have been. Traffic running southwest through Fells Point would have joined with the main arterial highway at this location. This elevated structure was demolished in the mid-1990s.

 The Design Concept Team's 3-A plan attempted to spare Fells Point with an elevated expressway passing behind many of the waterfront houses. Later they proposed removing the houses, building a tunnel and then putting the historic houses back in place. Planners would later come to realize that such mitigation between expressway and community would cost more than the city could afford. Estimates for the Fells Point-Canton corridor ranged from $609 million to $1 billion in the 1970s.

Protesters against the projected highways picket in front of Mayor D'Alesandro's home. In the wake of the assassination of Martin Luther King, Jr. and the ensuing Baltimore riots, Mayor D'Alesandro oversaw a city that appeared to be in constant crisis.

"IT'S THE *People's* MEETING"

Social worker and community activist Barbara Mikulski led a city-wide coalition of approximately 32 anti-expressway organizations called Movement Against Destruction (MAD). When Mikulski and another organizer Esther Redd invited U.S. Secretary of Transportation John Volpe to Baltimore to talk about the city's expressway plans, Volpe agreed. During that meeting at the Edmondson Community Center, Mikulski addressed Secretary Volpe, "This is not Barbara Mikulski's meeting…not Esther Redd's meeting…It's the people's meeting!…" Mikulski then presented the Secretary with a MAD "STOP THE ROAD" button.

Success at organizing coalitions and opposing urban highways sparked Mikulski's long career in politics. It led her to seats in the Baltimore City Council, the United States House of Representatives and eventually the United States Senate.

 This meeting at the Community Center on Edmondson Ave. February 5, 1972, with Barbara Mikulski as moderator and U.S. Secretary of Transportation John Volpe in attendance, put road builders on notice. Community resistance to urban expressways and the 3-A plan would remain steadfast. What had begun as a concern for preserving historic neighborhoods had grown into a concern to preserve Baltimore's ethnic and minority neighborhoods as well as its parkland. Activists reminded Secretary Volpe of the recently passed 1969 National Environmental Policy Act and invoked it to protect the Gwynns Falls Creek Valley and Leakin Park from the I-70 extension, a tactic that would prove successful.

THE *Gateway* THAT BECAME A DITCH

The most dramatic part of the 3-A plan was the construction of an I-70 spur, I-170, as a below-grade interstate with high retaining walls. I-70 was a transcontinental highway and its spur would be a grand entrance into the city, an east-west expressway. It would join with an elevated I-95 spur a mile from the Inner Harbor and an elevated I-83 spur in the central business district.

So impressive and elegant was the design of the planned joining of urban interstate spurs that it would carry its own interstate number. However, where highway planners had seen the grand eloquence of the Baltimore gateway, some Baltimore residents saw a skyline dominated by concrete and the loss of properties in the history-rich communities of Federal Hill, Fells Point and Canton. The I-170 "ditch" divided neighborhoods in the working-class Franklin-Mulberry corridor and hundreds of homes were condemned to build it. Protests followed and compromise routes ensued.

I-95 was rerouted through a tunnel, and the spur of I-83 inside the Baltimore Beltway was designated the Jones Falls Expressway and terminated before intersecting with I-95. However, the interstate spur that fared the worst came at the expense of I-70. Conservationists managed to thwart the I-70 spur in litigation, maintaining that it would do environmental damage to Gwynns Falls Valley and Leakin Park in West Baltimore.

Of the grand entrance into Baltimore, all that remains is 1.4 miles (renamed U.S. 40) and a "park and ride" just inside the Baltimore City line. However, the ghost of Baltimore's "road wars" still lives behind Jersey wall barriers that hide abandoned stub ramps, which are connected to nothing.

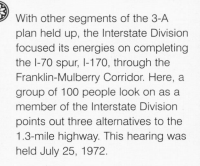

With other segments of the 3-A plan held up, the Interstate Division focused its energies on completing the I-70 spur, I-170, through the Franklin-Mulberry Corridor. Here, a group of 100 people look on as a member of the Interstate Division points out three alternatives to the 1.3-mile highway. This hearing was held July 25, 1972.

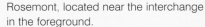

The Design Concept Team studied multiple routes for bringing I-70 through Leakin Park and Gwynns Falls Park. They settled on this alignment, but residents in the surrounding communities argued against it. Aside from the environmental impacts to the park, the I-70 extension would have strongly affected the middle class African-American community of Rosemont, located near the interchange in the foreground.

For 30 years, the dream of highway planners such as Herbert Fairbank and Robert Moses had been to coordinate public housing and expressway planning. This dream finally came to fruition in Baltimore when I-170 broke ground in 1974. Twenty years later, the high-density housing to the north and south of the freeway was torn down and replaced with low-density housing. Meanwhile I-170 never gained interstate status. It was re-signed as part of U.S. 40.

THE OTHER *"Road War"*

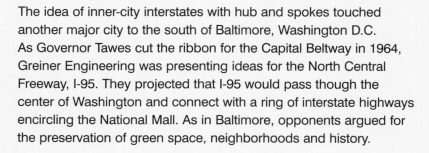

The idea of inner-city interstates with hub and spokes touched another major city to the south of Baltimore, Washington D.C. As Governor Tawes cut the ribbon for the Capital Beltway in 1964, Greiner Engineering was presenting ideas for the North Central Freeway, I-95. They projected that I-95 would pass though the center of Washington and connect with a ring of interstate highways encircling the National Mall. As in Baltimore, opponents argued for the preservation of green space, neighborhoods and history.

The "Save Takoma Park Committee" called this idea for the North Central Expressway, I-95, a "Berlin Wall" and demanded that SRC Chairman John Funk be fired. When other expressway opponents likewise fought against I-270 in Washington's northwestern Maryland suburbs, the SRC abandoned both routes. I-95 was later incorporated into the eastern half of the Capital Beltway.

In 1967, the Federal government appropriated funds to hire a Design Concept Team, a panel of architects, sociologists, economists and city planners to make recommendations on how to address the cultural and aesthetic priorities of Baltimore's residents. The result became a work in progress, but its essential recommendation was to bypass the central business district with innovative ways of meeting the city's transportation needs. This meant an interstate spur of I-95 that touched the edge of the central business district and connected with an at-grade limited-access "city boulevard" (named after Martin Luther King, Jr.), serving as an interface with the city's streets. The spurs of I-83 and I-70 were terminated well short of their planned rendezvous with I-95 in the central business district.

The Baltimore "road wars" of the late 60s were successful in areas like Federal Hill and Fells Point, because residents managed to get their houses on the National Register of Historic Places, but many Baltimoreans did not fare as well. Construction of the I-70 spur destroyed over 700 homes in the Franklin-Mulberry street corridor and hundreds of residents were displaced.

Writing in his 1963 memoir, *Mandate for Change 1953 – 1956*, Dwight Eisenhower predicted that the Interstate Highway System would "change the face of America." He was right, of course. The interstate became the engine of economic expansion, and it is difficult to envision America today without it. In fact, the interstate stretching broad and bold into the horizon is to this day a mainstay of American popular culture.

The Federal Highway Administration has amassed a list of hundreds of "road songs." A consistent theme in these songs is the highway as a metaphor for mobility and individuality. One suspects that these are the highways that take drivers to vacations both near and far.

But some songs are of highway laments. Perhaps these highways are the metaphor for city residents displaced by road construction or living in a "dead space" of shadows from elevated expressways, cloverleafs and access ramps.

In the 1960s, the lesson was learned that there is a price to be paid beyond the cost of construction for building interstates in cities. It's the homes taken by the wrecker's ball, displaced families, loss of neighborhoods, and the destruction of parkland and historically-significant buildings. Baltimore City concluded that's a price too dear. Surplus funds from Baltimore's "road wars" were redirected to other transportation projects.

Departments of Transportation were created both nationally (1966) and in Maryland (1970) to ensure that other means of transport (subways, light rail and buses) would be a part of future urban transportation systems.

Lasting IMPRESSIONS

 The Interstate Division of Baltimore drew upon the best and the brightest of the State Roads Commission, later the State Highway Administration, as well as Baltimore City's Department of Public Works. Bill Hellmann is shown third from left in this February 28, 1978 picture of the opening of a portion of I-95 from Canton Avenue to Russell Street. Other members of the Interstate Division are left to right, Richard Trainor, Duane Carter, Bill Hellmann, Harry McCullough, Kenneth Merrill and Dick Wardenfelt.

Bill K. Hellmann Looks Back on Baltimore's Road Wars

From 1984 to 1987 Bill Hellmann served as Maryland's chief transportation official, Secretary of Transportation, but a decade earlier he was a young man assigned to the Interstate Division for Baltimore City, and a front-seat observer of Baltimore's "road wars."

"We were able to accomplish a fair amount in a short period of time. We completed I-95 through Baltimore City, including the Ft. McHenry Tunnel. We completed I-395 and Martin Luther King, Jr. Boulevard. But we weren't able to complete the entire system as initially conceived. However, looking back on it, what got completed was what should have been completed. And what didn't get completed probably shouldn't have been completed. When you consider Leakin Park and its natural environment and the rebirth of Fells Point and Canton, there's no question that the ultimate decision was the right decision."

Cynthia Simpson

From 1968 to 1972, Cynthia Simpson was a Morgan State College (now Morgan State University) undergraduate majoring in sociology and anthropology. "I wanted to learn about people," remembered the Eastern Shore native. That's what piqued her interest in what was happening to the people, mostly African-American, who lived along the Franklin-Mulberry street corridor where homes were being destroyed to build an "East-West" interstate spur into Baltimore.

Ms. Simpson recalled that many displaced families moved to new homes in communities around the beltway, like Randallstown, and even farther to the northern suburb of Reisterstown, but what left a lasting impression from her student days was a neighborhood "torn apart" and a community "wiped out."

Cynthia Simpson never became a sociologist or an anthropologist; instead she became a highway builder herself, advancing to Division Chief of the State Highway Administration's Project Planning Division, a first for an African-American and a female. However, the memory of what happened to a once-thriving Baltimore community remained with her. As a supervisor and a mentor to young engineers, she drew on her memories of the Baltimore "road wars" and talked about the social repercussions of building a highway.

Cynthia Simpson

New highways – a promise to boost economy.

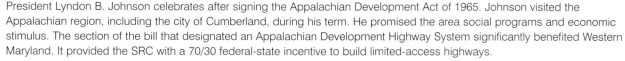

THANKS FOR A *Beautiful* **HIGHWAY**
ROUTE 40 ASSOCIATION

SRC efforts to upgrade U.S. 40 in the 1950s did not benefit from the generous 90/10 interstate funding formula. Instead, the federal government planned for construction of I-70 from Baltimore to Hancock. There, I-70 turned north into Pennsylvania. This left old U.S. 40 off the interstate map. The SRC made continuous upgrades, but interstate construction in the central regions of the state demanded the most attention.

President Lyndon B. Johnson celebrates after signing the Appalachian Development Act of 1965. Johnson visited the Appalachian region, including the city of Cumberland, during his term. He promised the area social programs and economic stimulus. The section of the bill that designated an Appalachian Development Highway System significantly benefited Western Maryland. It provided the SRC with a 70/30 federal-state incentive to build limited-access highways.

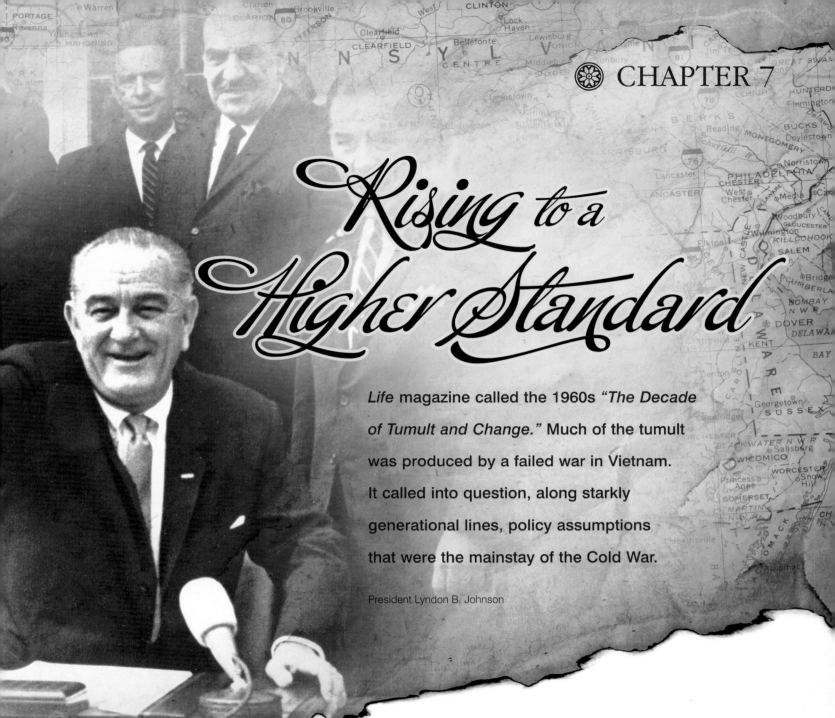

CHAPTER 7

Rising to a Higher Standard

Life magazine called the 1960s *"The Decade of Tumult and Change."* Much of the tumult was produced by a failed war in Vietnam. It called into question, along starkly generational lines, policy assumptions that were the mainstay of the Cold War.

President Lyndon B. Johnson

The rationale for the Interstate Highway System — moving urban residents out of, and troops around, cities devastated by nuclear war — was one of the 50s Cold War assumptions. Vietnam changed that. For the first time since Eisenhower was president, interstate highways would have to stand on their own.

There was nothing new about that in mountainous Western Maryland. The furious interstate building spree of the late 1950s and early 60s had bypassed that part of the state with only modest upgrades to U.S. 40, with minimal federal involvement being the order of the day. Consequently, Maryland's slice of Appalachia had never experienced the halo effect from a national commitment greater than transportation itself. That was about to change.

In 1965, President Lyndon Johnson's Appalachian Regional Development Act placed economic stimulation for the mountain counties of the East Coast at the center of the "Great Society." For the State Roads Commission, this meant a commitment to an interstate highway through the mountains. Economic, environmental, historic and social concerns would make it slow going, but in its first 10 years of effort from '65 to '75, the agency completed half of the high-speed route, linking Cumberland to West Virginia.

While full completion of the National Freeway would take until 1991, the post-Vietnam decades of the 1970s and 80s brought important engineering accomplishments with more immediate results. The two most spectacular achievements of those decades were both "seconds." The first of these was the construction of the second Chesapeake Bay Bridge.

The location of the original bridge at Sandy Point, outside of Annapolis instead of Baltimore, gave convenient access to the Eastern Shore to more than just Marylanders. Sandy Point is 35 miles directly east of Washington, D.C., and an easy commute if there were an express-way from Washington's Beltway and a bridge over yet another body of Maryland water, the Severn River. The State Roads Commission (SRC) put all three pieces of that puzzle togther in the 1950s.

By the 1960s it was clear that the Chesapeake Bay Bridge, opened in 1952, when combined with the construction of a new Severn River Bridge in 1953 and the upgrading of U.S. 50, was wildly successful in bringing Washington D.C. visitors to Maryland's Eastern Shore, and the town of Ocean City on the Atlantic Ocean in particular. Some said too successful.

In only 10 years, traffic volume doubled on the first Cheaspeake Bay Bridge, and its two lanes were overwhelmed with beach traffic during the summer. Fifty percent of that traffic came from Washington, D.C.

Traffic congestion was of epic proportions and could produce backups all the way to the Severn River, blocking entrances to Annapolis. In hindsight, a second bridge became a self-induced necessity when the Sandy Point location was chosen for the first bridge. The General Assembly argued about alternative routes as it had done when the first bridge was built, but ultimately the State Roads Commission was instructed to give priority to the same location for a second bridge.

Appalachian DEVELOPMENT AND THE

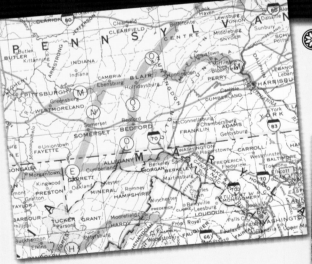

A section of the 1966 map designating the corridors for the Appalachian Development Highway System within Maryland. Corridor E can be seen running along U.S. 40 and U.S. 48. Corridor N runs along U.S. 219, and corridor O along U.S. 220. Corridor highways were intended to connect with interstates and create better access for the region. The original program covering 11 states ran from Pennsylvania to Alabama.

This November 1966 photo marks the opening of Cumberland's controversial thruway. Some said that it split the city in half. Others welcomed it as a conduit to progress and potential growth.

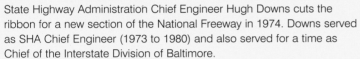 State Highway Administration Chief Engineer Hugh Downs cuts the ribbon for a new section of the National Freeway in 1974. Downs served as SHA Chief Engineer (1973 to 1980) and also served for a time as Chief of the Interstate Division of Baltimore.

A segment of the upgraded National Freeway crossing the Youghiogheny River in Garrett County.

National Freeway

 On November 13, 1975, SHA opened a 13-mile portion of the National Freeway, U.S. 48. This completed a 44-mile dual-lane, limited-access highway from Cumberland to the West Virginia border. Simultaneously, West Virginia celebrated completing a 27-mile section from the state border to Morgantown.

Taking a ride on the National Freeway, September 1974. The new limited-access highway west of Cumberland negotiated some of Maryland's most rugged terrain and became a welcome sight for many. But Western Maryland residents would have to wait another 15 years before the highway between Cumberland and Hancock was completed.

 The intersection of U.S. 50 and 301 south of Queenstown, 1950s.

U.S. 50 is the primary highway link between Washington, D.C. and Annapolis, and ultimately Maryland's Eastern Shore and the Atlantic Ocean. Attention naturally gravitates to the U.S. 50 crossing of the Chesapeake via the William Preston Lane Jr. Memorial (Chesapeake Bay) Bridge, an engineering accomplishment of world renown; but there is another story about U.S. 50 that's equally interesting.

U.S. 50 in Maryland was begun, and parts of it completed, as an expressway under Maryland's Expressway Act of 1947. Maryland was building expressways without at-grade intersections, the defining characteristic of the interstate, before there was an Interstate Highway System. However, what seemed forward looking from the perspective of the early '50s seemed less so when the federal contribution to interstate construction was pegged at 90 percent in 1956, rather than the previous share established at 50 percent.

U.S. 50 from Annapolis west to Bowie was already opened and a second portion from Bowie to Lanham was nearing completion by the time of the 90 percent funding formula. Nevertheless, expansions, upgrades and improvements of U.S. 50 would be eligible for 90 percent money if U.S. 50 had an interstate designation.

The challenge with making U.S. 50 an interstate highway is that U.S. 50 is a historic transcontinental highway from Maryland to California, and a section of U.S. 50 from Bowie to Queenstown also shares the same alignment with U.S. 301. The addition of more signage would be confusing for motorists, but was it worth the price of accessing interstate highway money?

The solution was to make U.S. 50 a spur of I-95 and give it an interstate highway designation, I-595. However, motorists wouldn't know it. There weren't — and as of this writing, aren't — any I-595 highway shields along U.S. 50.

The "unsigned" interstate status of U.S. 50 was intended to avoid the confusion of adding another highway number, but this historic route's identity isn't restricted to numbers. Between Annapolis and the Washington Beltway, U.S. 50 carries signage as the *John Hanson Highway* in honor of this country's first "president" under the Articles of Confederation. After the highway passes Annapolis on its way to the Chesapeake Bay via the William Preston Lane Jr. Memorial Bridge, it becomes the *Blue Star Memorial Highway*, in honor of the nation's armed services. Once securely on the Eastern Shore of Maryland, near Queenstown, the highway becomes the *Ocean Gateway*, and remains so all the way to its terminus in Ocean City. On Maryland's western edge, a small stretch of U.S. 50 runs through Garrett County. It's named the *George Washington Highway*.

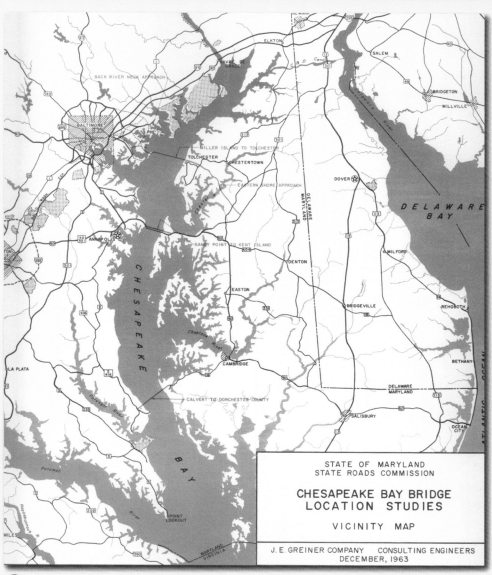

Traffic backups like those pictured here were common in the 1960s, particularly on weekends during the summer. The second Bay Bridge was to alleviate the backup problems by adding three additional lanes; however, an automotive breakdown or collision could still tie up traffic for hours.

In the 1940s, Maryland road-builders considered two ways to cross the Chesapeake Bay. A strong contender was the Miller's Island to Tolchester route, which would originate in Baltimore. The obvious advantage to this route was its access to Baltimore, but at 6.9 miles, it was also the longest route. A second route would originate from Sandy Point, outside of Annapolis. Like the Baltimore route, it made use of an island, Kent Island, as a terminus, but the distance was less, at 4.03 miles. In the 1960s, when the need for a second Bay Bridge was recognized, the J.E. Greiner Company proposed a third alternative, a bridge from Lusby in Calvert County to Taylor's Island in Dorchester County. However, like the Baltimore to Tolchester route, at 6.3 miles, the Calvert County route was longer than the Annapolis crossing. To keep things simple, the second Chesapeake Bay Bridge was built parallel to the first, from Sandy Point to Kent Island.

THE *Second* CHESAPEAKE BAY BRIDGE . . .

The second Chesapeake Bay Bridge was designed as a parallel alignment with the first, but with three lanes instead of two, giving a total of five lanes over the Cheasapeake Bay. Like its older sibling, the second Chesapeake Bay Bridge was an aesthetic and engineering success.

The center spans of both the first and second bridges are supported by large wire cables spun from thousands of smaller steel wires wrapped together. These cables are draped over high towers and then connected to great concrete-block anchorages. The road deck was hung with perpendicular steel wires connected to the cables. The resulting weight is distributed over the towers and pulls at the anchorage.

The concrete anchors are the key to these suspension bridges. Unfortunately, the bottom of the bay floor falls off where the anchors for the suspension spans of the second bridge were poured. The result was much deeper piers and more concrete to make them. One pundit said that there was enough concrete in those piers to fill Baltimore's Belvedere Hotel. Cost overruns ensued. Nevertheless, the second Bay Bridge opened on schedule in 1973.

The twin spans of the Chesapeake Bay Bridge are engineering marvels, but within 10 years the bridge was again vulnerable to summer traffic surges.

There are three lanes of U.S. 50 leading to the bridge in each direction. The '52 bridge span takes traffic eastward and the '73 bridge span takes it westward. U.S. 50's lanes can move 6,000 beach-bound cars an hour towards the two lanes of the eastward span, which can only move 4,500 cars an hour. The solution has been to divert some of the beach-bound summer traffic to one lane of the '73 span. This "contraflow" is governed by traffic cones and overhead traffic signals.

The Sandy Point to Kent Island location of the Chesapeake Bay Bridge proved superior for optimal utilization, but it also demonstrated that a good site location stimulates traffic. In a repeated scenario from 1952, the construction of the 1973 Chesapeake Bay Bridge has not proven sufficient for peak hour crossings.

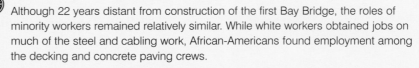
Although 22 years distant from construction of the first Bay Bridge, the roles of minority workers remained relatively similar. While white workers obtained jobs on much of the steel and cabling work, African-Americans found employment among the decking and concrete paving crews.

Construction workers stand on one of the bridge trusses before a barge floats it toward its final destination.

The second span of the Chesapeake Bay Bridge shares a similar alignment with the first span, but it is 450 ft. north, resulting in a slightly shorter shore-to-shore length (including causeway) of 4.33 miles instead of the first span's 4.35 miles. Its suspension bridge towers are taller, 379 ft. versus 354 ft., but the biggest difference between the two bridge spans is cost. The first, opening in 1952, cost $45 million; the second, opening in 1973, cost $148 million.

A concrete anchor pier during construction. The bay floor falls off where the anchors were poured for the suspension spans of the second bridge. The result was the need for much deeper piers and more concrete to make them.

A concrete anchor pier from the inside. Workers pump concrete into one of the massive piers used to anchor the suspension cables. One pundit said that there was enough concrete in the piers to fill Baltimore's Belvedere Hotel.

Bridge workers wrapping the strands of the bridge's suspension cable with protective aluminum casing.

Governor Marvin Mandel presides over opening day of the second Chesapeake Bay Bridge, June 28, 1973. In the front seat, left, is the new Maryland Department of Transportation Secretary Harry R. Hughes. The bridge construction started as a State Roads Commission project, but the Maryland Transportation Authority became its owner and operator.

...A *Hard Rain*

Hurricane Agnes happened at an unlikely time of the year and highlights the stress that weather can inflict on the state's transportation system. Agnes was born in the warm waters off the Yucatan Peninsula only a few weeks into the hurricane season and seemed little threat to Maryland when it made landfall on the Florida Panhandle on June 19, 1972.

There were no record-breaking winds or storm surges from the Category-One hurricane. Agnes moved northeastward in Maryland's direction, but concern was minimal because hurricanes usually lose strength when they travel over land. Agnes weakened to a depression over Georgia, but then an ominous turn of events occurred.

From eastern North Carolina, Agnes darted into the Atlantic, refreshing her intensity. The storm returned to land soaked with water and merged with a non-tropical low on June 23. The combined system poured record rainfall over the Mid-Atlantic states until June 25. "Agnes rewrote the book on inland flooding and the impact a tropical storm can have hundreds of miles from the coast," said Sol Summer, Hydrology Division chief at the National Weather Service Eastern Region.

The Chesapeake watershed was inundated with rain and rivers rose to historic levels. The swollen Patapsco River blocked every transportation route southward out of Baltimore. For only the third time in its history, every gate of the Conowingo Dam was opened to prevent it from being swept away by the cresting waters of the Susquehanna. A total of 28 bridges and culverts of the state highway system were destroyed and there was another unwanted distinction as well. Maryland had the highest per capita death toll of the five Mid-Atlantic states declared a disaster area by President Nixon.

Hurricane Agnes swept through Maryland in June of 1972, destroying more than 28 bridges throughout the state, including this one on Reisterstown Road.

On U.S. 29 near White Oak, Silver Spring, SHA workers respond, but it would take more than five years before all the bridges were in working order again.

MD 410 East West Highway, Prince George's County.

THE *Thomas Johnson Bridge*

Officially opened in January of 1978, the Thomas Johnson Bridge is 135 feet tall at its highest point and joins Calvert and St. Mary's counties. The two-lane bridge was completed at a cost of $26 million and cuts driving time from Lexington Park to Solomon's Island from 90 to 10 minutes.

On June 23, 1972, during the days of Hurricane Agnes, Chief of Bridge Design Albert Leslie Grubb drove to the Washington suburbs to give advice on bridges taken by the storm. Head of the bridge department for 25 years, Grubb was a man passionate about bridges. Fellow employees speculate that the stress of losing so many bridges may have contributed to his passing that same night of a heart attack. A native of West Virginia, Grubb had taken over the bridge department in 1948. There have only been four bridge chiefs in the 100-year history of the agency, Walter C. Hopkins (1920 to 1948), Albert L. Grubb (1948 to 1972), Howard "Hank" Bowers (1972 to 1974) and Earle "Jock" Freedman (1974 to present).

The Grubb Bridge? Not exactly. Although named the Thomas Johnson Bridge after Maryland's first governor, consideration was given in 1977 to naming this bridge after SHA's long-serving bridge chief. Albert Grubb had worked tirelessly for a bridge over the Patuxent, but having it bear his name wasn't to be. A naming panel objected and the governor's name won out.

The second of the post-road-war years' accomplishments was a consequence of the road wars themselves. Like the first Bay Bridge, the first tunnel under Baltimore's harbor was over capacity within 10 years after it was built. Its dual lanes were overwhelmed by traffic. As with the Bay Bridge's beach-bound traffic, the cause of the Harbor Tunnel's inadequacy was easily identified. It was

motorists on I-95 seeking an alternative to the Baltimore Beltway to bypass the city.

The cause célèbre of the 1960s road wars was interstate highway spurs merging in Baltimore's central business district. The spur merge was designed to provide suburban access to the city, but it also offered I-95 access through Baltimore via a bridge that passed over the harbor

from the Locust Point Peninsula. The Locust Point Peninsula is home to historic Fort McHenry; in fact one of the proposed bridge's piers would have been on fort property. The construction of a bridge next to Fort McHenry, whose defense of Baltimore in 1814 was the inspiration for Francis Scott Key's *Star Spangled Banner*, outraged historic preservationists.

BUILDING THE *Fort McHenry* TUNNEL

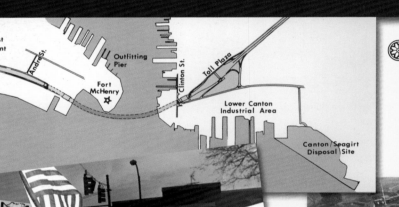

Construction on the 1.7 mile Fort McHenry Tunnel began in 1980 and was completed in five years. The tunnel curved around the south side of Fort McHenry and under the Baltimore Harbor navigational channel. Its alignment required the first tunnel sections in the world that were curved both horizontally and vertically.

Locust Point residents and preservationists alike were outraged in the early 70s to learn that highway planners proposed a double-decker bridge adjacent to historic Fort McHenry, which inspired Francis Scott Key to write the *Star Spangled Banner*. The Interstate Division of Baltimore took a second look, and in 1975 the tunnel proposal spared the historic site.

As with the first Harbor Tunnel, the immersed-tube construction technique was used. Tugboats towed the steel tunnel segments down the Chesapeake Bay to Baltimore where they were sunk in a dredged trench.

An innovative solution was called for, and one was forthcoming. The bridge became a tunnel under the Baltimore Harbor with four lanes in each direction.

The Fort McHenry Tunnel, named after the national monument and historic site that led to its creation, completed the final link in I-95, the nation's most heavily traveled north-south interstate highway.

Construction and design was administered by the Interstate Division for Baltimore City. The Interstate Division for Baltimore City successfully designed the I-95 connection with city residents and historically significant buildings in mind. When completed in 1985, the Fort McHenry Tunnel left the residential communities of Locust Point and Fells Point untouched, and it rescued Fort McHenry

from an urban highway landscape.

Traffic studies projected that the Fort McHenry Tunnel would not generate sufficient revenue to offset its costs. The studies were wrong. The Fort McHenry Tunnel exceeded revenue estimates and is now the most profitable toll facility operated by the Maryland Transportation Authority.

Completing the I-95 Corridor
The construction of the Fort McHenry Tunnel completed the I-95 corridor, which is a 1,917-mile long north-south artery for vehicle traffic between Maine and Florida. The I-95 Corridor Coalition begun in 1993 is a multi-state alliance whose goal is to enhance transportation mobility, safety and efficiency through the coordinated management of transportation operations.

Engineers inspect a tunnel segment under construction in Port Deposit, Maryland, on the Susquehanna River.

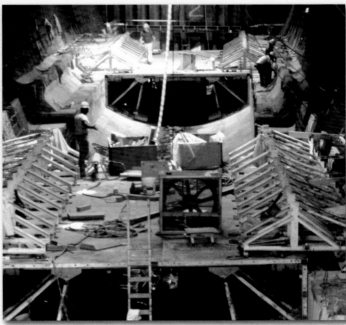

"A bit of wisdom." A construction worker stands alongside a cutting drill used to dredge the Patapsco River for the tunnel project. When dredge spoils from the river were relocated to construct the Seagirt Marine Terminal, the process demonstrated the true flexibility of a state department of transportation.

The construction of the Fort McHenry Tunnel cost $750 million. This was $75 million less than the original construction estimates and a welcome change from the second Bay Bridge experience.

After the tunnel tubes were sunk, workers constructed the road surface. The tunnel's ventilation shafts were placed within the tube cavities below.

There was another positive aspect to the Fort McHenry Tunnel. The 3.5 million cubic yards of material dredged out of Baltimore Harbor to make room for the tunnel's prefabricated sections were used to create the 146-acre Seagirt Marine Terminal. A veteran of those days, Bill Hellmann, considered it the highlight of his career and a "win-win situation" for both the traveling public and the Port of Baltimore.

Unlike some cities' ports, the port has always been part of how Baltimore viewed itself. Building I-95 under the harbor helped preserve Baltimore's commercial viability and its identity. It might not have turned out that way. When Seagirt opened for business, Transportation Secretary Richard "Dick" Trainor pondered that "there will be some hard decisions to make if what we're doing now doesn't work." But work it did, and today the Seagirt Marine Terminal is a showpiece of high-technology containerized cargo handling.

Maryland's love affair with interstate highways faded from the days when Eisenhower was president. In retrospect, it's obvious that such an immense undertaking would be susceptible to community resistance, like Baltimore's road wars, and cost overruns as happened with the second Bay Bridge, but outright scandal was a shock to Marylanders.

Maryland's experience with a highway-related scandal was not the worst of the interstate era, but it was by far the most public in road building history. In fact, it led to the resignation of the Vice President of the United States, former Maryland Governor Spiro Agnew.

As the County Executive in Baltimore County, Spiro Agnew began the questionable practice of accepting money from engineering consultants who did road work. He brought the practice to Annapolis when he was elected governor. Whether this was a customary fundraising practice for political campaigns, as Agnew maintained, or kickbacks from consultants seeking state work, as the U.S. Attorney in Maryland alleged, it became a moot point when Agnew failed to report income he had received from consulting engineers on his 1967 income tax report. Rather than face a trial, Agnew entered a plea of no contest (*nolo contendere*) and agreed to pay what was owed the Internal Revenue Service in back taxes. He was sentenced to three years' probation and fined $10,000. Agnew resigned as Vice President. That earned him the dubious distinction of departing office with a criminal record. It also cast a shadow over the State Roads Commission.

Given the longevity of the SRC, the massive amounts of money entrusted to it and the many consultants and contractors employed to do road work, there had been remarkably few scandals in SRC history. In 1928, it was discovered that employees in the Purchasing Department had stolen $376,000 through fictitious supply and material purchases. They were sentenced to terms in the state penitentiary. A citizens' committee appointed by Governor Albert Ritchie found that the corruption was limited to the individuals convicted, but the SRC commissioners, including John Mackall who held the combined posts of chairman and chief engineer, resigned.

In 1956, a right-of-way engineer confessed that he had been paid $8,500 by two Washington real estate investors.

They used inside information to acquire property in planned right-of-way routes and then sold it for a quick profit. The SRC engineer was dismissed and the real estate agents convicted of conspiracy and fined. A subsequent investigation found no other state employees involved and new procedures for right-of-way acquisitions were developed. These scandals were venal and straightforward. The scandal that tarred the SRC through association with Spiro Agnew, when he was Maryland's governor, was more complex.

The SRC commissioners were appointed by the governor and served at the governor's discretion, without Senate confirmation. In theory, this tied accountability directly to the governor, who is accountable to the people. In practice, it invited politicizing into road building. At the very least, this is what Governor Spiro Agnew was doing when he appointed his long-time aide, Jerome Wolff, as the Chairman of the SRC in 1967.

The SRC consisted of six part-time regional commissioners and a full-time chairman. The chairman hired engineering consultants, and they were treated differently from the contractors who built Maryland's highways and bridges. Engineering consultants were not required by law to be the low bidder to acquire state work, but were selected on the basis of qualifications. Then a negotiated price followed.

There is a fine line between demanding kickbacks from engineering consultants doing state work and the "common practice" of asking consultants for political contributions. In exchange for limited immunity, Wolff became a government witness who testified that Agnew had crossed that line.

Two Road Officials Resign in Maryland

Ritchie to Name Entirely New Commission; $376,000 Shortage Bared.

Baltimore, Jan. 8 (A.P.).—Gov. Ritchie tonight had the duty of naming an entire new State roads commission.

Two members, R. B. Darnall, of Ruxton, Democrat, and W. W. Brown, Republican, gave the governor their resignations today. The post of commission chairman had been vacant since Gov. Ritchie decided to separate the posts of commission chairman and chief engineer and retain as engineer John N. Mackall, who had held both positions. The governor appointed Oscar F. Lackey to be chairman, but Mr. Lackie died before he could take up his duties.

The resignations followed completion of an investigation showing a shortage of $376,000 in road funds through larceny and embezzlement by employes of the commission, and Mr. Darnall explained that he was resigning to give the governor a free hand in reorganizing the commission.

 The scandal of 1929 involved employees in the SRC Purchasing Department. Governor Ritchie appointed the Nelligan Commission to investigate, and it produced a report on July 30, 1929, requiring improved accounting procedures. While SRC Chairman and Chief Engineer John N. Mackall was not implicated directly in wrongdoing, Governor Ritchie asked him and the other commission members to step down.

Gov. McKeldin Plans to Name Roads 'Czar'

Removal of Present Commission Head Seen in Shakeup

By Frank R. Kent Jr.
Staff Reporter

Reorganization of the Maryland State Roads Commission with appointment of a $25,000-a-year "czar" to be in charge of the state's network of highways and its half-billion-[dollar] year progra[m]

Suspension Of DuPre Is Disclosed

Ben DuPre, assistant right-of-way engineer for the Maryland State Roads Commission, is under suspension because of complaints on SRC land purchases in Montgomery County, it was learned yesterday.

The road official, who participated in acquisition of some $6 million in private property for the new Washington National Pike and intercounty belt freeway in Montgomery and Prince Georges Counties was suspended by the commission effective June 10.

Joseph D. Buscher, assistant attorney general for the road agency, said the suspension was made at his recommendation but declined to elaborate on

THE EVENING SUN

CITY AND STATE SECTION

• FINANCIAL
• LOCAL NEWS

• METRO
• NEWS

PAGE D 1

BALTIMORE, THURSDAY, OCTOBER 11, 1973

PAGE D 1

Case Against Agnew: Contract Kickbacks

AFTER DINNER—The former vice president heads for car after having dinner at a Little Italy restaurant. Mr. and Mrs. Vernon Nash watch from steps of their home

 A right-of-way scandal in 1955 involved the purchase of properties along U.S. 240, today's I-270. This revealed the potential for SRC right-of-way agents to pass insider information along to land developers. As a remedy, the SRC implemented a new program to freeze property values before purchases and inaugurated its real estate department. As had happened in 1929, although no SRC Commissioners were involved in the scheme, Governor McKeldin replaced the entire body.

In 1973, several years after Governor Agnew and State Roads Commissioner Jerome Wolff left state government, federal prosecutors determined that Chairman-Director Wolff had acted as a middleman in a kickback scheme involving engineering consultants and the former governor. Wolff later provided evidence against Agnew and described how money had been exchanged for guaranteed contracts.

Following these revelations, the State Highway Administration revamped its system of awarding consultant contracts. It set up an independent consultant review panel requiring that consultants submit technical and bid proposals to win contracts. Despite the high profile of what became known as "the Agnew scandal," the fraud involved totaled about $150,000, or less than half of the figure discovered missing in 1929. While there can be no excuse for corruption in government, clearly the climate of public scrutiny had reached a new level. Agnew ended up repaying the state $248,000, including interest.

$\mathcal{R}i\delta e$ OF THE "DOTs"

"In a nation that spans a continent," President Lyndon Johnson said, "transportation is the web of Union." The web that Johnson created in the Department of Transportation Act of 1966 brought together 31 federal agencies and bureaus, including the Bureau of Public Roads. There was more than administrative efficiency behind the creation of the Department of Transportation; it was a reaction to the environmental movement and state road wars, like the one in Baltimore. The first Secretary of Transportation, Alan Boyd, added a fitting epitaph for the car culture when he said: "We want an end to the noise, pollution, and general disfigurement transportation has unintentionally brought to our cities."

 Lowell Bridwell helped author legislation that created Maryland's Department of Transportation. He began his career as a newspaper reporter, but in 1967, he succeeded Rex Whitton as Federal Highway Administrator. From 1981 to 1984, Bridwell served as MDOT Secretary and is shown here at the opening of I-795 in 1982.

One of the last meetings of the State Roads Commission before the creation of MDOT and the State Highway Administration. The new organization became effective on July 1, 1971.

Left to right, Secretary of the Commission Austin W. Smith; SRC Chief Engineer Walter Woodford; Special Assistant Attorney General and the Commission's Attorney Joseph Buscher; Commissioner Walter Boucher; Chairman-Director David Fisher (with back to camera), Executive Secretary for Maryland Highway Contractors Association William Hardy and Commissioner Harley Brinsfield.

In 1970, the Maryland General Assembly created its own transportation department, the Maryland Department of Transportation. Of all of the state DOTs, Maryland's was the most expansive in providing the tools for a multi-modal approach to transportation. One reason is Lowell Bridwell, a Federal Highway Administration veteran of President Johnson's transportation reforms, who served as a consultant.

A cabinet level officer, the Secretary of Transportation was given responsibility for all of the revenue and bonding authority that had existed with separate state transportation agencies, like the State Roads Commission. The Secretary administered an all-inclusive Transportation Trust Fund. With all tax-based transportation revenue, including the gas tax, deposited in one fund, the link between user fees and revenue expenditures was cut. In addition, the Secretary of Transportation was the ex officio (by virtue of one's office) chairman of the Maryland Transportation Authority (MdTA), which issued bonds and collected toll revenues. The toll revenues were pooled, giving flexibility to use them for maintenance and capital improvements for all MdTA transportation projects. Maryland's flexible approach to transportation management was bold and without precedent among the state DOTs. MDOT's first Secretary, Harry Hughes, said: "We've got the best law in the country and a chance to build a balanced, integrated transportation system." Lowell Bridwell agreed.

 Governor Hughes cuts the ribbon for the Fort McHenry Tunnel. Front row left to right, Congresswoman Helen D. Bentley, Executive Director of FHWA Les Lamm, Mayor William Donald Schaefer, Maryland House of Delegates Speaker Benjamin Cardin, Governor Hughes, Baltimore City Councilman William J. Myers, and City Council President Clarence H. "Du" Burns.

Agnew's plea of "no contest" to income tax evasion seemed to sidetrack a day of reckoning on the issue of consultant kickbacks. However, in 1981, a Maryland court ordered that he repay $248,000 to cover bribes he took while in office.

What Agnew understood to be business as usual had resulted in a deterioration of public trust. Repairing that damage required structural changes — review procedures to eliminate opportunities for unethical transactions and the full disclosure of all political contributions by highway consultants and contractors — and an exceptional act of political courage.

In 1970, the General Assembly created the Maryland Department of Transportation (MDOT). Its first secretary was a veteran Eastern Shore legislator, Harry R. Hughes. As Secretary of Transportation, Hughes provided focus for previously independent and often competing state transportation needs. However, it wasn't Secretary Hughes' appointment at MDOT that left a lasting impression. It was the way he left it.

Harry Hughes restored integrity to transportation when he resigned as Transportation Secretary rather than

award a subway construction contract to a politically favored firm. At a time when Maryland transportation might have acquired a reputation for cronyism, Hughes placed transportation on the high ground of principle. It was what the transportation community wanted; Maryland citizens wanted it too. They elected Harry Hughes governor in 1978 with more than 700,000 votes, at the time a total unmatched by any other gubernatorial candidate in Maryland history.

Changing of the guard...

James J. O'Donnell and David Fisher attend a meeting of the Maryland State Roads Commission. Fisher became the Assistant Secretary of the Maryland Department of Transportation. Deputy Secretary of Transportation O'Donnell served as Acting State Highway Administrator before the appointment of Bernard Evans.

 David H. Fisher served as the last Chairman-Director of the State Roads Commission and the first State Highway Administrator under MDOT. Here, he stands before a map of Maryland's seven highway districts and welcomes members of the newly formed Transportation Commission to State Highway headquarters.

Formed in 1971, the Maryland Transportation Commission studies the state transportation system and advises the Secretary of Transportation and department administrators on policy and programs. The commission has 17 members. Ten are appointed to three-year terms by the Governor with the advice of the Secretary of Transportation. The seven regional members of the State Roads Commission serve ex officio.

State Highway Administrator Bernard Evans presents MDOT Secretary Harry Hughes with a highway map, the first to bear a logo for the newly formed Maryland Department of Transportation. Hughes appointed Evans, a former district engineer in Pennsylvania, after a national search.

A-Changin' Times

CHAPTER 8

The muse of the 60s, popular poet/singer Bob Dylan, proclaimed that the times were a-changin', and a big part of that was the work of a transplanted Marylander, Rachel Carson.

Rachel Carson was a Johns Hopkins-trained biologist who worked at the Bureau of Fisheries, only the second woman hired at that agency. She lived in Silver Spring. During the 1940s, Carson wrote books about life in the sea, a subject that few Americans knew much about before her popular works on the subject. In the 50s, she became a full-time writer. It was at that time that she began her seminal work, *Silent Spring*, which was published in 1962.

In *Silent Spring* Carson created a sobering scenario, a silent spring when no birds sang because they had been poisoned by pesticides. *Silent Spring* was about chemical pollutants, not roads, but its popularity was rooted in deeper themes: mankind losing its moorings to the natural world, corporate/government hubris and the unintended consequences of technology. These themes cast a broader net than over pesticides. They gave birth to the environmental movement, which quickly expanded from chemical pollutants to the airborne pollution of automobiles, the impervious surface of highways and the global warming of the earth.

In the 10 years following the publication of *Silent Spring*, a host of environmental legislation was passed by Congress. The automobile culture as it had evolved over the 20th century would not be the same again. Cars and the roads they traveled on were accused of causing air pollution, numbing the senses with gaudy highway advertisements, poisoning the environment and destroying rare species of plant and animal life.

In 1963, Congress passed the Clean Air Act, setting strict pollution standards for industry. In 1965, automobile emissions were added to the clean air list. In 1970, an amendment to the Clean Air Act mandated a 90 percent reduction in tailpipe emissions for the '75-'76 car model year. The words "catalytic converter" became as important as the word "horsepower" in automobile vocabulary.

Against the background of congressional enthusiasm for clean air, President Lyndon Johnson's wife Claudia (aka "Lady Bird") urged Congress to improve the view. She lobbied Congress for federal standards limiting billboard

Lady Bird AND HIGHWAY BEAUTIFICATION

SRC Landscape Bureau Chief Charles Anderson attends a reception held by Lady Bird Johnson at the White House, January 19, 1966. On this evening, Mrs. Johnson entertained members of the Committee for a More Beautiful Capital to discuss strategies for beautifying Washington entry roads. Only a few years before, several members of the committee had helped defeat I-270's entrance into D.C. When it came to highway beautification, however, they found common ground with Anderson and the SRC.

From left to right, front row: Admiral Neill Phillips, Ms. Polly Shackleton, Mrs. James Rowe, Secretary of the Interior Stewart Udall, Mrs. Johnson, William Walton, and Walker Stone; second row: Rudolph Kauffmann, Mrs. Alfred Coiner, Commissioner Walter N. Tobriner, Knox Banner, Adam Rumoshosky, and Skidmore, Owings and Merrill architect Nathaniel Owings; third row: SRC Landscape Bureau Chief Charles Anderson (not a member of the committee), Katie Louchheim, Walter E. Washington, T. Sutton Jett, (behind Washington), William Schmidt, and Charles Horsky. Mrs. Philip Graham, also a member of the committee, was not present when the picture was taken.

Rachel Carson, a resident of Silver Spring, published *Silent Spring* in 1962 and ushered in the environmental movement. "Without this book, the environmental movement might have been long delayed or never have developed at all," said former Vice President Albert Gore in his introduction to the 1994 edition of *Silent Spring*.

advertising and screening junkyards along interstate and federal-aid highways. Not since Eleanor Roosevelt had a first lady taken such a high profile on a regulatory issue.

The State Roads Commission's (SRC) Landscape Department worked closely with the first lady in developing beautification practices that went beyond billboards and junkyards. They built noise barriers and pioneered erosion and sediment protection practices. The Landscape Department also planted wildflowers. Lady Bird liked flowers, and they became the focus of her efforts to make Washington, D.C. a more attractive capital. "Masses of flowers where masses pass," Lady Bird wrote in her diary.

Whether it was the involvement of the first lady in the legislative process, or what some saw as the ephemeral nature of planting flowers, opposition was vocal, and Congress required a rare late night session to pass the Highway Beautification Act of 1965. In derision, critics of the legislation called it the "Lady Bird Bill," but it made a difference in Maryland. In 1934, in the heyday of unregulated highway advertising, there were 39 billboards per mile on U.S. 1. After the "Lady Bird Bill," the average fell to 16 billboards per 10 miles on federal-aid roads. In 1988, the House of Representatives honored Lady Bird for her efforts in preserving the scenic beauty of American highways.

THE *Look* OF THE *Ride*

Tree planting on the Capital Beltway between the Wisconsin and Connecticut Avenue exits. Landscape Bureau Chief Charles Anderson worked closely with Mrs. Johnson on highway beautification after construction of the Capital Beltway.

While the Highway Beautification Act placed some emphasis on planting along highways, early emphasis was on eliminating junkyards and billboards. Former SRC Landscape Bureau Chief Charles Anderson recalled another part of its legacy:

"The first two years we got money, I thought it was more important that we acquire scenic lands rather than spending it on planting. Most of these areas were wooded. Then later on, I went before the commission, and I got the money to buy scenic lands all along the Kennedy Highway. That's why you don't see a lot of development along the highway."

SCENIC BYWAY

CHARLES STREET

When Lyndon Johnson signed the *"Lady Bird Bill,"* he said it would "bring the wonders of nature back into our daily lives." In Maryland, that proved to be prophetic in a way that Lady Bird would appreciate. Maryland's wildflower program began in 1986 as an effort to reduce mowing, decrease air pollution, provide wildlife habitat and reduce stormwater runoff. Each year, SHA plants hundreds of acres of wildflowers along highway shoulders and medians.

Maryland's scenic byway program has evolved over the years. Chosen routes are not only scenic, but also emphasize the state's historic, natural, archeological, and recreational heritage. The U.S. Department of Transportation recognizes the Catoctin Mountain Scenic Byway, the Chesapeake Country Scenic Byway and Maryland's portion of the Historic National Road in its prestigious category of "America's Byways."

 Junior Assistant Highway Engineer and later Resident Engineer for District 1 Charles Albert Skirven is doing some "big tree moving" in 1940. Attempts to look at landscape and environmental issues as an integral part of the road system began in the 1930s. These early efforts had to be functional. Landscape improvements might be used to control erosion, reduce headlight glare, delineate curves or redirect drifting snow. The 1965 Highway Beautification Act allowed landscape designers to integrate functional safety requirements with highway aesthetics.

Before the development of high-speed freeways, scenic overlooks like this one at Sideling Hill gave motorists a break. Along U.S. 40 in Western Maryland, it was often said that truck drivers could check their brake lights as they rounded the hairpin turns. Picnic areas and scenic overlooks provided a good place to pull over when driving anxiety ran too high.

On the far left wearing a suit, SRC Landscape Engineer Sylvester "Bud" Baumiller directs the spraying of fertilizer on a new slope cut. Baumiller started his career as a motorcycle policeman, then transferred to the SRC and began handling landscape duties in the 1930s under the Bureau of Maintenance. On October 14, 1970, the SRC and the Federated Garden Clubs of Maryland dedicated the eastbound rest area on I-70 between Frederick and Hagerstown in his honor.

Yet another marriage of highways and aesthetics is the designation of "scenic byway" to roads that travel through Maryland's most spectacular countryside or highlight its historically significant sites. There are nearly 2,500 miles of scenic byways in Maryland. The Catoctin Mountain Scenic Byway, the Chesapeake Country Scenic Byway and Maryland's part of the Historic National Road are in the prestigious category of "America's Byways," a designation by the U.S. Department of Transportation for a unique cultural asset.

"Adopting" a few miles of highway isn't a grand gesture, but it's a practical way that Marylanders can improve the appearance of their highways. "Adopt-A-Highway" is for businesses, civic groups, schools and even families. They "adopt" up to three miles of roadway by picking up litter four times a year for a two-year period, and highway signage acknowledges the good stewardship of the participants. The related "Sponsor-A-Highway" program offers Maryland corporations an opportunity to fund litter pickup where high-traffic interstates pose too great a danger for volunteers.

The adopted and sponsored highways may never qualify as scenic byways, but motorists can thank the volunteers and sponsoring businesses for making the ride litter free.

In some ways, nurturing the aesthetic component of Maryland highways is even older than the highway beautification efforts of Lady Bird Johnson. It harkens back to the days between the World Wars, to the days of Maryland "show roads," when transportation was as much about the journey as the destination.

While Lady Bird was beautifying highways, Congress was working on nothing short of a national policy to "stimulate the health and welfare of man." The law was called the National Environmental Policy Act of 1969 (NEPA).

NEPA language left highway engineers scratching their heads, but in fact the intent of NEPA wasn't to define the "welfare of man," but to require that federally funded projects like highways be evaluated in terms of their impact on the environment. Specifically, road-builders were required to draft

"environmental impact statements" that entered environmental issues into the public dialogue. For the first time, the environment joined funding issues and technological feasibility as a major consideration in building roads.

In 1973, Congress added the Endangered Species Act to the list of considerations that impacted federal funding for highways, and "critical habitats" became a factor in highway design. The concept of "endangered species" was acknowledged by Congress in 1966. The Secretary of the Interior was told to keep a list of what they were, and in 1973 highway planners were told not to build highways through their habitats. Ironically, this sometimes meant taking the homes of people in order to leave the homes of their non-human neighbors intact.

Clearly, the times were a-changin' from the years when Dwight Eisenhower was president, and it wasn't just the highways, but the workforce that built and maintained them as well.

Environmental STEWARDSHIP

A multidisciplinary team of geotechnical engineers, intermodal planners, road designers and environmentalists conduct a preliminary investigation for road improvements and impacts on a nearby stream. SHA personnel includes Howard Johnson (far left) of the Regional and Intermodal Planning Department.

When the U.S. Congress passed the National Environmental Policy Act (NEPA) in 1969, no highway agency in the country knew what to do with it. It came with no guidelines or directives. Before NEPA, highway planners put roads through flood plains and wetlands because that was the path of least resistance. After NEPA, the objective was not to affect those habitats.

The first environmental impact statement (EIS) written for a Maryland State Highway project was for an 18-mile section of U.S. 113 on the Eastern Shore. The document was 15 pages long and authored by Harry Dorsey, a man trained as a highway engineer. Fifteen years later, a similar project along U.S. 113 required an EIS document of 150 pages. EIS reports have only gotten longer over the years, incorporating more legislative directives and requiring a new industry of planning and consulting related to environmental mitigation and stewardship.

Environmental Planner Lou Ege recalled, "It took six years before we could produce an EIS document that meant anything." Ege came to the agency as a graduate from a teacher's college and expected to do highway work for a year or two until he found a teaching position. After 30 years, he retired from the agency and now works as a consultant. "There were no environmental people then. I worked on the EIS for the National Freeway in Western Maryland in the 1970s and never once visited Western Maryland. Nobody went out into the field to check. We didn't have the personnel to do it. Today, that's unheard of."

SHA employees (including Ed Stein at left) investigate environmental mitigation steps taken during road construction in Central Maryland. The stormwater retention pond in the foreground and silt fence in the distance demonstrate that after NEPA, erosion and sediment measures are taken not only when the project is completed, but throughout construction. SHA was the first agency in Maryland to develop temporary sediment and erosion control measures on construction sites. Other state and county agencies used early SHA reports as templates.

A group of environmental consultants install "bed load sampling traps" on the Northwest Branch of the Anacostia River. The sampling traps measure sediment conditions in a stream that will later be restored, part of the mitigation effort taken for construction of the Intercounty Connector.

SHA personnel from across the disciplines attend Chesapeake Day on the Bay, 1996. Sponsored by the Chesapeake Bay Foundation, SHA staff followed the course of rainwater from Eastern Shore roads to the bay, becoming better acquainted with how road construction affects the bay's watershed.

Left to right, Bernie Saggese (Highway Design), Keith Kucharek, unknown man, Jeff Magerian, Richard Zeller, Linda Mott (Environmental Design), Jan Taylor (Construction Inspection), Michelle Arnold (Construction Inspection), Mel Stickles, Tom Lidard (Federal Aid), Matt Zulkowski (Bridge Development), Ralph Manna (Bridge Development), Will Baker of the Chesapeake Bay Foundation, Ken McDonald (Highway Development), unknown man in sunglasses facing right and Joe Milchenski (Construction Inspection).

❁ The Kent Narrows Bridge, completed in 1986, illustrates one of the primary changes in bridge design after NEPA. Aside from eliminating a draw span, the higher and longer bridge passes over as much land as it does water, accommodating the breadth of the 100-year flood plain. Should flooding occur, the bridge height will allow rising water on either side of the tidal stream an unimpeded flow. The older bridge, left in place to serve local traffic and recreational purposes, will probably not fare as well.

❁ This mound of earth depicts the SRC's first attempt at noise mitigation. Located west of Georgia Avenue, the SRC created this earth berm to block highway noise not long after construction of the Capital Beltway. The barrier was later replaced by a wooden sound wall, and by the late 1980s, a textured concrete sound wall.

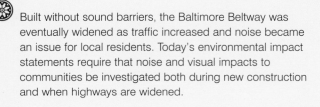

❁ Workers assemble a textured sound wall along the Baltimore Beltway near Harford Road in the late 1980s.

❁ Built without sound barriers, the Baltimore Beltway was eventually widened as traffic increased and noise became an issue for local residents. Today's environmental impact statements require that noise and visual impacts to communities be investigated both during new construction and when highways are widened.

SHA Architectural Historian Anne Bruder (with drawing board) and members of the Maryland Historical Trust (MHT) document an early 19th century springhouse in northern Baltimore County. Also shown in the photo are MHT Administrator of Research and Surveys Marcia Miller, Architectural Historian Fred Shoken and MHT Administrator of Architectural Research Thomas Reinhart.

Along with environmental issues, SHA's Environmental Planning Division includes a Cultural Resources Section. Consideration of cultural resources on highway projects began in 1969 under State Archeologist Tyler Bastian's supervision, when SHA borrowed archeologists from the Maryland Geological Survey (MGS) to address impacts on archeological sites. As had happened nearly 75 years before when the SRC was founded, MGS soon transferred members of its staff to the highway agency.

Archeologist Carol Ebright examines a 3,000-year-old fragment of Native American soapstone pottery, in 1989. Quite often, potential road construction projects provide the impetus for discovering Maryland's cultural heritage.

For the first 50 years of SRC history, African-Americans might work on maintenance crews and as contract laborers, but none had worked as an engineer or technician within SRC headquarters. Many of the first African-American men to earn professional positions within the SRC had a few things in common. Most were veterans of the armed forces, who had served either in the Korean conflict or WWII. In other instances, they had either graduated from college or taken college classes.

One such employee, Abraham Pettit, a graduate of the historically black A&T College in North Carolina, also took graduate courses at Columbia University in New York. For an agency with a tradition of hiring recruits out of high school and then training them in-house, men like Pettit were more than well qualified.

A contemporary of Pettit's, Van Yerrell, can be credited as the first African-American to obtain an engineering position at the agency. Yerrell came to the SRC in 1954 as a Marine veteran of both WWII and the Korean War. He had

BREAKING THE *Color Barrier*

The first African-American to obtain a professional position at the highway agency was Van Yerrell. Yerrell came to the SRC in 1954 as a Marine veteran of both WWII and the Korean War. Yerrell had attended North Carolina A&T College and worked for the SRC's Bureau of Road Design.

A contract worker or "teamster" along the Urbana Pike in 1920. For the first 50 years of SRC history, African-Americans might work on maintenance crews, in district shops and as contract laborers, but none had worked as an engineer or technician within SRC headquarters.

Rudolph C. Cane obtained employment as an SRC Evaluation Engineer in 1957, working in the Bureau of Materials and Research. In the mid-1960s, Cane helped establish the SRC regional laboratories and in 1968 transferred to the Eastern Regional Lab, where he performed soil testing for the second Chesapeake Bay bridge. After retiring as the regional lab's Director of Administration in 1984, Cane pursued a political career and won election to the Maryland House of Delegates, serving District 37A on the Eastern Shore.

also attended A&T College in North Carolina and earned a position in the SRC's Bureau of Road Design. After 21 years with the agency, Yerrell transferred to the Interstate Division in Baltimore in 1971. He worked on such projects as the Franklin-Mulberry street corridor and what was then called City Boulevard, but which we know today as Martin Luther King, Jr. Boulevard.

Few professions had been less hospitable to women than bridge or highway work. Some women did attain professional positions in road planning and inspection in the 60s and 70s, but they were depicted as an oddity worthy of press coverage. A story about Susan Camp (now Cortese), an SRC road inspector, told of the "lipstick wearing" inspector who was a "petite, blue-eyed

blonde." *The Sun* newspaper assured its readers that Marion McCoy, the SRC's first professional planner, was an "attractive auburn-haired woman." Another pioneering female who came to the agency in the early 1960s, but one who never gained newspaper coverage, was Nancy Knipple, a draftsperson in the Bureau of Bridge Design.

Edward Tombs obtained employment in the Bureau of Locations and Surveys in 1957. Segregated facilities throughout Maryland during the late 50s and early 60s prevented Tombs from traveling the state with his white coworkers and visiting job sites. For this reason, Tombs spent much of his early career working within the headquarters building.

John Harris (far right) joined the Bureau of Locations and Surveys in 1961. Harris cites his work as a laborer on the U.S. 40 bridge over the Monocacy River in the late 50s as inspiration for pursuing work with the SRC. Other locations and surveys workers in the photo include, left to right, Engineering Associate VI Albert Oster and Area Location Engineer Frank Koller Jr.

William Walker, pictured with coworkers on the Bureau of Road Design softball team, became the first African-American at headquarters to appear in an SRC publication, *The State Roadster*, August 1957. Walker was among a handful of African-American men who began to obtain technical jobs within the main office. He remained with the agency only until the early 1960s.

Standing left to right: Robert Lewis, William Walker, Vernon Goodwin, Irvin Hughes, Thomas Ballou and Edward Kimmey. Kneeling left to right: Ronald Meyers, Kirk Logan, Leonard Zembas, James Yeager and Edmund Wright.

SEIZING THE *Opportunity*

Raleigh Medley came to SHA in 1971 and worked in the Annapolis maintenance shop. Over the years, his hard work earned him promotions until he became the first African-American to attain the position of Assistant District Engineer for Maintenance in the SHA District 3 office. District 3 comprises Prince George's and Montgomery counties and is often considered the busiest and most challenging SHA district. Medley retired in 2004 after a 33-year career.

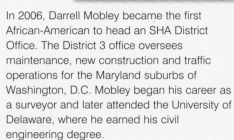

In 2006, Darrell Mobley became the first African-American to head an SHA District Office. The District 3 office oversees maintenance, new construction and traffic operations for the Maryland suburbs of Washington, D.C. Mobley began his career as a surveyor and later attended the University of Delaware, where he earned his civil engineering degree.

SHA Deputy District Engineer of District 3 Wesley G. Mitchell began his career with SHA in the Project Planning Division as a project engineer in 1997. His past duties have included developing preliminary engineering plans and coordinating projects with citizens' organizations. More recently, Mitchell managed the preparation of the environmental impact statement for the Intercounty Connector (ICC) project.

Working first as a photographer for the Maryland Traffic Safety Commission, then the State Roads Commission, and today the State Highway Administration, Timothy Hyman has traveled every corner of the state. His career spans six decades and includes the days of Maryland's segregated past. Nevertheless, "Snapshot" Tim, a nickname given by his colleagues, has documented every major Maryland construction project of the last half of the 20th century, including the Washington and Baltimore beltways, Chesapeake Bay bridges and Baltimore Harbor tunnels one and two. The secret of his longevity: "You have to remember this," Hyman says. "You are not being paid to be liked or disliked. You are being paid to do your job. Do that and people will gravitate to you."

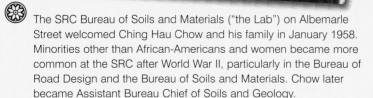

The SRC Bureau of Soils and Materials ("the Lab") on Albemarle Street welcomed Ching Hau Chow and his family in January 1958. Minorities other than African-Americans and women became more common at the SRC after World War II, particularly in the Bureau of Road Design and the Bureau of Soils and Materials. Chow later became Assistant Bureau Chief of Soils and Geology.

Women REDEFINE THEIR ROLES

THE STATE ROADSTER

 District 3 Resident Engineer and future SHA Administrator M. Slade Caltrider and his secretary Mrs. Ellen Adcock illustrate the more traditional roles of men and women at the agency up to the 1970s. While men held administrative and engineering roles, women worked as secretaries, shop clerks, radio operators and data processors. One or two had begun to work as engineers or planners in the 1960s.

 The State Roadster, a magazine for SRC employees, reveals the biases of 1960 on the cover of its summer issue. Aside from being "our cover girl," The Roadster told its readers that Miss Marlene Vendetti was a secretary in the department of Special Operations, competing against three other "cover girls" from the secretarial pool to become Miss State Roadster. The State Roadster lionized its cover girls in rhyming couplets such as: "With high ideals — yet gay and carefree, an ideal wife and mother she'll be."

Glen Burnie Woman To Plan New Roads

Annapolis, Jan. 31 — Mrs. Marion J. McCoy, assistant planning administrator of Anne Arundel county for the past four years, has been hired by the State Roads Commission as the agency's first professional planner.

The 33-year-old Mrs. McCoy lives in the Dundee area of Glen Burnie.

Mrs. McCoy was graduated from Ohio State University with a Bachelor of Science degree in geology, then did two years of graduate work in civil engineering.

While in graduate school in 1950-1951, she was assistant to the chief petroleum geologist for the State of Ohio.

From 1951 to 1953, she was a research associate with the mapping and charting research laboratory of Ohio State University. It was during this period that she married Eugene McCoy, an electronics engineer.

Arrived In 1954

They came to Maryland in 1954, when Mrs. McCoy joined a company that was designing roads for the State under contract. She worked on the first State highway

MRS. MARION J. McCOY

design prepared through the use of aerial photography.

The attractive, auburn-haired woman was employed by the Planning and Zoning Department of Anne Arundel county in 1956 and two years later became assistant planning administrator.

While with the county, she studied night courses in planning and planning statistics at Johns Hopkins University.

 When Marion McCoy joined the SRC Planning Department in 1962, it was news enough to make the Baltimore *Evening Sun* newspaper. Trained as both an engineer and lawyer, McCoy stayed a few years before moving on. *Evening Sun*, January 31, 1962.

121

Women IN THE WORKFORCE

Construction Inspector Deborah Huth began working in the mailroom for SHA in 1984. She took the Engineering Technician I test and started with the Construction Inspection Division the following year. Here, she records construction progress on the U.S. 40 bridge over the B&O railroad north of Rossville Boulevard.

Lipstick-Wearing Road Inspector Happy With Work

In 1977, Construction Inspector Susan Cortese proved a curiosity to one *Baltimore News American* reporter. The reporter had gone to check construction progress on the Key Bridge and discovered the progress being made within SHA culture. Cortese was shown working on the approach roads to the bridge. After a 30-year career at SHA, Cortese retired in 2007 after completing work on the I-695 and U.S. 40 westside interchange.

Linda Kelbaugh shown here in October 1989 being recognized for her work on MD 100. Kelbaugh began working for the SRC as a secretary in December of 1967.

Kelbaugh attended night school, earned a degree in environmental planning, and began working in SHA's emerging Environmental Programs Division. Having retired in 1996, she works as a vice president for the engineering firm of Greenman-Pedersen Inc. Also in the photo above, Steve Hawtof (far left) and SHA Administrator Hal Kassoff.

In 2007, Melinda Peters was appointed to lead the combined SHA/MdTA/private sector multi-disciplinary team that is designing and constructing the Intercounty Connector (ICC) Project. The $2.45 billion project includes design and construction of approximately 18 miles of six-lane highway. Peters is SHA's first female senior manager in an engineering capacity and manages more than 1,000 people.

Pictured above, the Women's Transportation Seminar (WTS) Baltimore Chapter WTS Members. Founded in 1977, WTS is an international organization of more than 4,000 transportation professionals — both women and men — with 42 chapters in the United States, Canada and Great Britain. WTS creates new opportunities and advances the careers of women in transportation, both in public and private industries.

Back row left to right: Denise Hagans, Glenn Litsinger, Marisol Peralta, Sarah Gary, Windy Dorn, Jessica Klinefelter, Kerri Corderman, Alan Straus, John Contestabile. Front row: Christine Wells, Janie Tiedeman, Katharine Arnerand and Karen Saab.

When SHA hired Gayle Seward as an auditor/trainee in 1976, she was the only female in a professional position in finance. She recalls one puzzled engineer asking why a "girl" was calling to audit his invoice, and even her supervisor was reluctant to send her on overnight business trips. Gayle Seward went on to become Director of Finance, the first female senior manager. She retired after a 30-year career.

After graduating from college in the early 1970s with hopes of becoming a teacher, Gail Jager decided instead to take SHA's technical exam. Her high score earned her a position as draftsman at a time when the term "draftsperson" had yet to be coined.

"It was a 'good old boys' club", she recalled. "The pinups were notorious. The guys watched me for a reaction. My answer was a big Sylvester Stallone poster. A lot of the guys complained. But my boss said that the Italian Stallion got to stay until their posters came down."

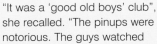

History was made when Hal Kassoff selected Elizabeth L. Homer as the first woman to serve as SHA's Deputy Administrator in 1990. Liz's long career at the Maryland Department of Transportation included leadership roles at headquarters and the Mass Transit Administration. She retired in 2001 and her successor, Ricky Smith, was the first African-American to be appointed to the high level leadership position. Since then, Administrators Parker F. Williams and Neil J. Pedersen appointed numerous minorities and women to senior posts.

In the 1980s, the American Association of State Highway and Transportation Officials (AASHTO) wanted to increase the number of college graduates with civil engineering degrees. A task force, headed by Maryland's State Highway Administrator Hal Kassoff, came to the conclusion that "the underlying problem was that not enough young people were going into civil engineering in the first place." AASHTO launched TRAC, the Transportation and Civil Engineering Program, aimed at junior high school and high school students.

Equipped with TRAC PACs, hands-on learning tools, AASHTO volunteers went to the secondary schools to, in Kassoff's words, "convey the excitement we felt, and still feel, about our profession." The Federal Highway Administration (FHWA) viewed TRAC as something other than a way to recruit civil engineers. The FHWA viewed it as a strategy to increase women and minorities in the workforce.

Vanessa Braddy, a veteran African-American engineer who started her road-building career in Maryland in the mid-80s, recalled that even in the 80s it was "tougher being a woman than being African-American." "Now," she said, "a good third of the project engineers are women." In fact, the most expensive miles of highway ever planned for Maryland, the Intercounty Connector between Montgomery and Prince George's counties, has a female project director, Melinda Peters. That's a-changin' attitude from the 60s and 70s.

In 1983, Elizabeth Dole became the first female Federal Secretary of Transportation, the highest ranking transportation official in the United States. In 2006, Mary Peters, former head of the Federal Highway Administration, became the U.S. Secretary of Transportation. The journey to respect for women in road building was a long time a-changin', and it started with a few proud and determined women in the 60s and 70s.

The turbulant decades of the 60s and 70s redefined how the nation viewed transportation. In 1973, Congress passed a federal-aid highway act that allowed money for abandoned projects supported by the Highway Trust Fund, like Baltimore's urban interstate spurs, to be reallocated for mass transit projects. Construction of the Baltimore Metro began with these reallocated highway funds.

The image of the interstate highway was tarnished in the 60s and 70s. Also worth remembering is that those who traveled on them rode on the most dependable and safest roads ever built. Design flaws

Opportunities IN THE 1970s

Gretchen Boyd, also shown in the group photo at left, served 35 years in SHA's Construction Inspection Division before retiring in 2007. As a road inspector in the 70s, Boyd recalled contractors who were rude. However, "I was still their inspector," she said, "and when there was a decision between yea or nay, then they realized maybe it's to their advantage to treat the inspector okay. They had to learn that."

Ten African-American recruits receive certificates after completing the first SHA-engineering associate training program, September 1974. These recruits received training in basic technical and engineering principles as well as practical experience.

   Participating in the graduation ceremonies were (left to right) Franklin Ward, Bruce Thompson, Gretchen Boyd, Charles Pack, Patricia Greene, William Sullivan, Highway Administration Office Director Patrick H. Dionne, Evelyn Green, Emily Burton, and SHA Internal Equal Opportunity Unit Officer Arnold M. Jolivet. Also participating in the program but not present for the ceremony was Deborah Weckesser.

like "suicide curves" faded from public memory and guardrails and breakaway lampposts became so common that they were taken for granted.

Goods and services followed Maryland's interstate highways, which opened access to all parts of the state. If Maryland motorists voted by the choices they made in highway travel, the interstate would be a hands-down winner. While interstate highways comprise a mere 1.6 percent of Maryland's roadways, 30 percent of Maryland vehicle miles are traveled on them.

The State Roads Commission did not emerge from the 60s and 70s the way it had entered. In fact, the SRC as a road-building agency didn't emerge at all. In 1970, the Maryland General Assembly ended the long solo run of the SRC by creating the Maryland Department of

Transportation (MDOT), which combined previously separate state agencies dealing with all varieties of transportation into one agency. The SRC road building function became an MDOT modal administration and was renamed the Maryland State Highway Administration (SHA).

In the modern era, the SRC exists in the shadow of its former prominence, with property condemnation proceedings being its most important function. There are seven part-time commissioners, representing geographical areas, appointed to five-year terms by the Secretary of Transportation with the Governor's approval. The SRC chair is the State Highway Administrator.

If you follow the money, you can see the change in mindset from both sides of the turbulent decades of the 60s and 70s. In

the late 1950s, the SRC had exclusive access to transportation funds and its own bonding authority. By the 1980s, revenue from fuel taxes, vehicle excise taxes, motor vehicle fees and federal aid were pooled together into one multi-purpose Transportation Trust Fund for a variety of highway and non-highway uses. Going into the 60s, the talk was about an "Interstate Highway System." Coming out of the 70s, the talk was about a "Comprehensive Transportation Plan." Going into the 60s, federal funding focused on engineering feasibility. Coming out of the 70s, sociological and environmental impact could trump even the best-designed highway. A-changin' times saw the end of unbridled highway "boosterism," and the beginning of broader thinking that included not only highways, but also transportation by rail, water, air, as well as bicycles.

Outreach EFFORT

Affirmative action programs in road building began in Maryland in 1978. The goal was to increase the number of minority-owned contractors who received state contracts. The Maryland effort was called the Minority Business Enterprise (MBE) Program and the federal version, the Disadvantaged Business Enterprise (DBE) Program.

In 1995, the MBE percentage required on Maryland projects rose from 10 to 14 percent of a total contract, and in 2001, that requirement went up again to 25 percent. SHA leads many other state highway agencies in MBE compliance; however meeting goals has never been easy. President of the Maryland-Washington Minority Contractors Association, Wayne G. Frazier explains, "The profession of engineering does better, but in the heavy construction industry, the vast majority [of minority contractors] can't afford to purchase or lease the equipment they need to be competitive."

High school students from Garrison Forest High School construct a star-shaped bridge to compete in the first annual Transportation and Civil Engineering (TRAC) Competition. Co-sponsored by AASHTO and SHA, the program was designed to interest young people in civil engineering and transportation careers. This 1997 competition included students from Cardozo, Garrison Forest, Northwestern, Notre Dame Preparatory, Parkville and Perry Hall high schools.

Frazier says that many heavy construction companies go back several generations, while minority companies have only recently begun to see the same opportunities. "The entry amounts are great," he says. "Minority firms often compete in areas of clearing and grubbing or hauling. They work as subcontractors to larger firms. SHA has done a huge job reaching out, but there still are not that many skilled trades."

New points of departure.

With an energy crisis and inflation, MDOT encouraged Marylanders to use public transportation and ride-share. Above, a packed bus on the streets of downtown Baltimore City, and at left, a Park 'N Ride in Prince George's County.

 Governor William Donald Schaefer and State Highway Administrator Hal Kassoff celebrate opening day of the Sideling Hill Exhibit Center, August 2, 1991, the same day SHA officially opened I-68. With the governor's philosophy of "Do It Now" and Kassoff's ability to get things done, the two oversaw the completion of the interstate program. They also oversaw an improvement of state routes unparalleled since the days of SRC Chairman John N. Mackall and Governor Albert C. Ritchie.

CHAPTER 9

The Modern Era

Governor Schaefer traveled the state on his bus, promoting both the mountains of Western Maryland and the beaches of the Eastern Shore. SHA and MDOT made sure that travelers would find both regions easily accessible.

The change of the decade from the 60s to the 70s is a convenient point of departure from the history of roads in Maryland to Maryland roads in the modern era. It's when Congress put the federal road-building agency (the Bureau of Public Roads) under a newly-created U.S. Department of Transportation (DOT) and the Maryland General Assembly did the same thing with the State Roads Commission, creating the Maryland Department of Transportation (MDOT). The American Association of State Highway Officials acknowledged the trend towards "DOTs" by adding a "T" to its acronym, becoming the American Association of State Highway and Transportation Officials (AASHTO – pronounced "ash-toe").

From the conventional point of view, the creation of the DOTs occurred when suburban sprawl, air pollution and urban "road wars" overtook America's love affair with cars and interstates.

Before he became MTA Administrator, Walter Addison (left) worked as the SRC's Bureau Chief for Traffic and Safety. Some pundits disliked the idea of a highway engineer heading up the new Mass Transit Administration, but Addison was fully committed to developing a state-of-the-art public transportation system for Maryland's largest urban area. Securing funding from the state legislature would prove more difficult, however. Here, Addison and MDOT Secretary Hughes show off their choice for Baltimore City's new subway car.

In his new role as MTA Administrator, Walter Addison oversaw the planning of Baltimore's subway as part of a truly integrated intermodal system. The southern leg of the subway would have risen above ground and served Baltimore-Washington International Airport. Alignment for this track would resurface years later as a piece of the region's light rail system, as would the line traveling due north.

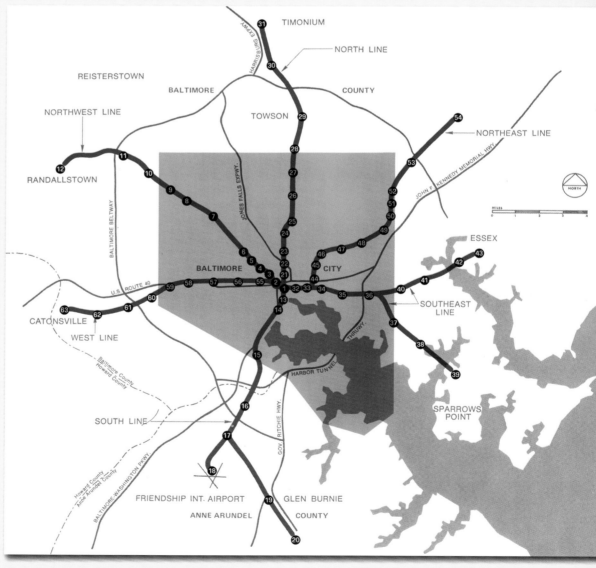

 Baltimore's Metro subway line is state of the art, but it's also small. Pictured above is a subway train leaving the Lexington Market Station. The entire Baltimore Metro subway system is 14 stations operating over 15.5 miles between Owings Mills in Baltimore County and the central business district. By way of comparison, Washington, D.C.'s Metrorail subway system has grown to five lines, consisting of 86 stations spaced over 106.3 miles. The cost of the Baltimore Metro was $1.39 billion.

However, the year the average Marylander will remember as the beginning of the modern era is more definitive — it's 1973. That was the year of the Oil Crisis, the year that Arab petroleum exporting countries embargoed sales to western nations supporting Israel in the Yom Kippur War, and the year that the price of gas went from 30 cents a gallon to more than a dollar and one had to wait in line to buy it. It was also the year that the federal government lowered the speed limit to 55 miles per hour.

There has always been a link between American highways and the "national interest." Army trucks destroyed Maryland's roads to get to the Port of Baltimore in the national interest during World War I. Congress skipped funding state highways in the national interest during World War II. And, during the Cold War, Congress paid for 90 percent of the cost of interstate highways; it was in the national interest to have exodus routes for city dwellers in case of a nuclear attack. Given all of that, it isn't surprising that the national interest would focus on the nation's automobile-based culture after 1973.

Mass transit was a logical alternative to automobiles for some, because urban residents used mass transit before there were affordable cars. By far the most nostalgic of these early forms of mass transit was the streetcar. In Baltimore, streetcars owned by private companies operated under a franchise from the Public Service Commission and there were even inter-urban electric lines between Baltimore, Annapolis and Washington.

Streetcar companies made money, at least until the automobile became more affordable. By 1935, only one streetcar company, the Baltimore Transit Company, remained and it phased out streetcars in favor of buses. In 1963, the last streetcar line in Baltimore was abandoned and even privately run buses were disappearing.

In 1970, the state salvaged what was left of private mass transit by purchasing the assets of the Baltimore Transit Company. Buses became publicly owned and put under what would become an MDOT modal administration in 1971, the Mass Transit Administration, later renamed the Maryland Transit Administration (MTA). The MTA is one of the few state agencies in the country that has total responsibility for local transit services in a major metropolitan area.

It was said that what the threat of nuclear war did for interstates, the fear of another oil crisis would do for mass transit. In anticipation of the migration from cars to mass transit, the Federal-Aid Highway Act of 1973 allowed states to relinquish Highway Trust Fund money in favor of an equivalent amount from the general fund for mass transportation. Federally subsidized mass transit systems were touted as the answer to dependence on foreign oil and automobile-induced gridlock on American highways.

At the very top of the mass transit apex of light rail, buses and trolleys is a subway system. After the oil embargo, a state-of-the-art subway system became the sign of a world-class city. Subway service became available to the Maryland suburbs of Washington, D.C. in the late 70s when the Capital's Metrorail opened stations in Montgomery and Prince George's counties. However, the Baltimore Metro subway did not open until 1983. It was expanded into a 15.5-mile subway line that connected Owings Mills in Baltimore County and the central business district. The Baltimore Metro was far smaller than the 70-plus miles of subway line that some urban planners said was needed, but it sought to make up for its small size by coordinating access with a light rail station at Lexington Market. The light rail was opened in 1992, expanded in 1997, and provided 30 miles of new generation "streetcars" with connections to BWI Thurgood Marshall Airport and Penn Station. Penn Station provided access to MARC, a Maryland commuter rail service, and Amtrak's northeast corridor.

Mass transit in Maryland was widely endorsed, but it wasn't without controversy. Suburban counties feared crime imported by trains from Baltimore, and in rural counties many believed that subways drained away money better spent on highways. In addition, trains were more expensive than highways, and tolls on roads and bridges made money, while reaching even a 50 percent return on mass transit was an elusive goal.

An inconvenient truth of intermodalism was undeniable. Marylanders did not embrace mass transit as a substitute for their cars. A trip on any Maryland interstate was evidence that automobiles remained the preferred method of transportation. More cars meant a public demand for more high-speed access roads serving the farthest reaches of the suburbs.

Enter the exurbs. Exurbs are communities located beyond the suburbs. The average Marylander might only recognize them by the names of shopping malls located there, but they had more than that in common. They were low-population density "bedroom communities," whose residents commuted to jobs in Baltimore or Washington or their suburbs, and they were almost totally dependent on cars.

In the 1970s the exurban communities between Baltimore and Washington, D.C. were growing fast. Existing interstate and Maryland routes could barely keep pace with increased traffic. When Hal Kassoff became SHA Administrator in 1984, he heard the appeals from county residents and officials to relieve clogged roads and synthesized the requests into a single concept. His idea was to build new highways, widen and limit at-grade crossings on old ones, and provide mass transportation options within a grid-specific plan. What became known as the Baltimore-Washington Transportation Grid created an arterial structure of highways connecting Baltimore, Washington, Frederick and Annapolis.

Some officials may have flinched at the thought of being a place on a grid between cities, but they had to admit that this regional approach to planning would give their residents the best chance of getting what they desperately needed — a convenient way to get to work.

BALTIMORE-WASHINGTON TRANSPORTATION GRID

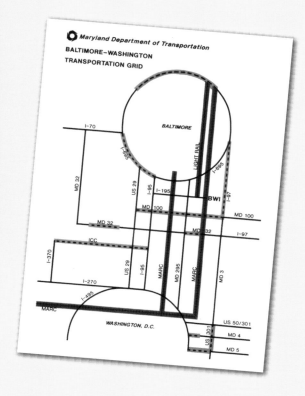

 SHA Administrator Hal Kassoff, serving from 1984 to 1996, presents his plan for a unified transportation system linking the Baltimore-Washington areas. What Kassoff called the Baltimore-Washington Transportation Grid was a network of limited access roads that tied two major cities together and provided access points to bus, subway and MARC commuter trains. Kassoff presented the plan to officials in Anne Arundel, Baltimore, Howard, Montgomery and Prince George's counties during annual MDOT tours.

For much of the modern era, Hal Kassoff was the face of Maryland highways. Kassoff had a 25-year career with the Maryland Department of Transportation, including 12 years as the State Highway Administrator. Many post-interstate era road-building initiatives were begun under his leadership, including controlled-access highways, inter-modal connections with mass transit, priority lanes for buses and carpools and greater use of technology to create safer and more efficient roads.

Kassoff's ascendance to the top job at SHA marked a distinct break with past appointees. He brought the sensibilities of a planner and preservationist to his position. In the 1960s, he had taught planning courses for the Federal Highway Administration. Later, he worked for

the Maryland Department of Transportation in the Washington region when the agency was attempting to extend I-95 and I-270 into the heart of the city.

Kassoff notes that when the I-95 project was canceled, the $300 million dedicated to it went back into the Transportation Trust Fund. When that money wasn't used for transit, 1970s double-digit inflation grew the amount to $2 billion. When Kassoff became SHA Administrator, the money was available for roads. "Out of the $300 million credit," he says, "we built I-97 from the beltway to Annapolis; U.S. 50 from the Capital Beltway to Annapolis; I-195, a road to the Baltimore-Washington Airport; and I-370, which will be the first leg of the Intercounty Connector."

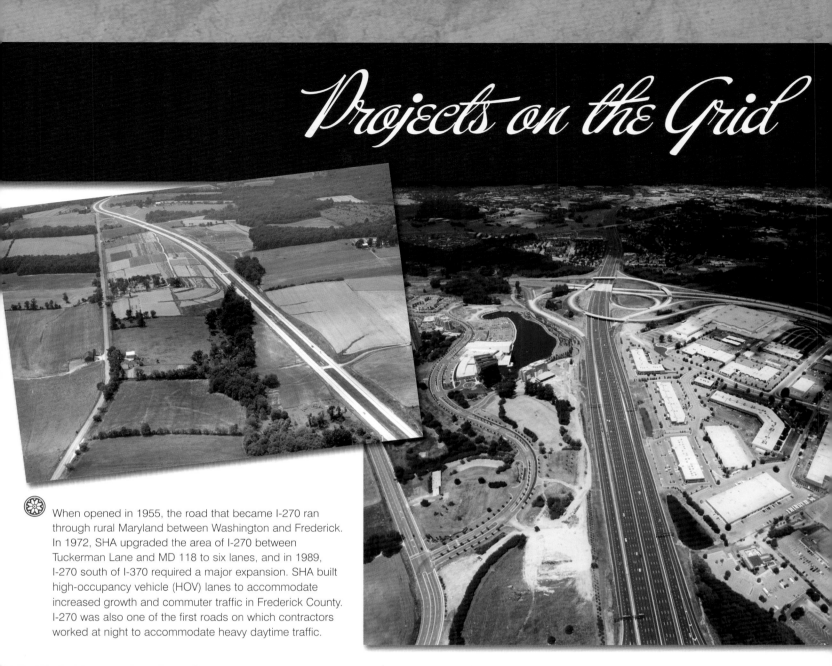

When opened in 1955, the road that became I-270 ran through rural Maryland between Washington and Frederick. In 1972, SHA upgraded the area of I-270 between Tuckerman Lane and MD 118 to six lanes, and in 1989, I-270 south of I-370 required a major expansion. SHA built high-occupancy vehicle (HOV) lanes to accommodate increased growth and commuter traffic in Frederick County. I-270 was also one of the first roads on which contractors worked at night to accommodate heavy daytime traffic.

Three-mile long I-370, running left to right in this photo, was built as a link between I-270 and the Shady Grove Metro station and completed in 1990. Transferring from automobile to subway provides commuters coming from the Frederick area with an alternative mode of getting to offices in Washington, D.C. I-370 will begin the western leg of the Intercounty Connector.

133

An increase of commuter traffic on the north side of the Baltimore Beltway called for added lanes. These photos show the Dulaney Valley Road interchange as originally constructed and after the completed expansion to six lanes.

In their day, Crain Highway (MD 3) and Ritchie Highway (MD 2) were the best paved roads in Maryland. By the 1970s, both of them were lined with houses and strip malls and often clogged with traffic. I-97 was planned to divert traffic from Ritchie Highway between the Baltimore Beltway and Annapolis, and from Crain Highway through Crofton and Bowie.

This 1950s photo of U.S. 29 between Clarksville and Columbia depicts the predominant farmland of Howard County before Jim Rouse created his new town of Columbia in 1967. By 2000, the population of Rouse's new town had soared from its original 8,000 residents to almost 90,000. Keeping pace with Howard County development, SHA gradually upgraded U.S. 29 to a limited access highway. The accompanying photo shows U.S. 29 at the MD 108 interchange in 1987.

Fully opened in 1993, I-97 avoided towns and suburbs and provided swift travel between Baltimore and Annapolis. At 17.62 miles, I-97 is one of the shortest two-digit interstates in the nation. When a proposed spur of I-97 going from Crofton to Bowie, I-297, met with community opposition, it was later abandoned. A major opponent of the I-297 spur was Anne Arundel County Executive O. James Lighthizer, who later became MDOT Secretary of Transportation.

County, state and federal government officials celebrate the opening of I-195 in 1990. I-195 provides an important link to BWI Thurgood Marshall Airport from I-95 and from the Baltimore-Washington Parkway.

Left to right, District Engineer for District 5 Edward H. Meehan, SHA Administrator Hal Kassoff, Howard County Councilman C. Vernon Gray, Maryland State Senator for Anne Arundel County Michael J. Wagner, FHWA Executive Director Dean Carlson, MDOT Secretary Richard H. Trainor and Maryland Aviation Administrator Theodore E. Mathison.

Limited access — MD 100 between MD 103 and the Snowden River Parkway. Within the Baltimore-Washington Transportation Grid, MD 100 provides a critical east-west link from I-97 in Anne Arundel to U.S. 29 in Howard County. The total cost for MD 100 was $307 million and its final segment opened November 23, 1999.

WHERE OPPORTUNITY TAKES OFF!

BWI BUSINESS DISTRICT

With the Baltimore-Washington Parkway on the western edge and the new I-97 on the eastern side, Anne Arundel County executives saw the potential to develop a business district between two major highways.

Travelers to and from BWI Thurgood Marshall Airport enjoy the convenience of an easy pick-up and drop-off loop at the end of I-195.

Workers spread asphalt pavement on a shoulder of MD 100. In contrast to the 1950s and 60s when Maryland built predominantly concrete highways, many of the new cross-county expressways were constructed with asphalt. By the 1980s, asphalt had become a competitive, if not predominant, road surface for new construction and in 1996, the Maryland Department of Transportation (MDOT) adopted the Superpave (SUperior PERforming Asphalt PAVEments) binder specification. Developed by the Federal Highway Administration, Superpave performs well under extremes of temperature and heavy traffic loads.

At 51.79 miles from Crownsville to Westminster, MD 32 is the longest east-west road on the grid, joining Anne Arundel with Carroll County. Upgrades for the portion known as the Patuxent Freeway, from MD 108 in Howard County to I-97 in Anne Arundel County, occurred throughout the 1980s and 90s. This photo shows completion of a diamond interchange in 2005 crossing MD 32 at MD 198 and Mapes Road. The interchange serves military facilities at Fort Meade and replaced the last signalized intersection along the freeway's length.

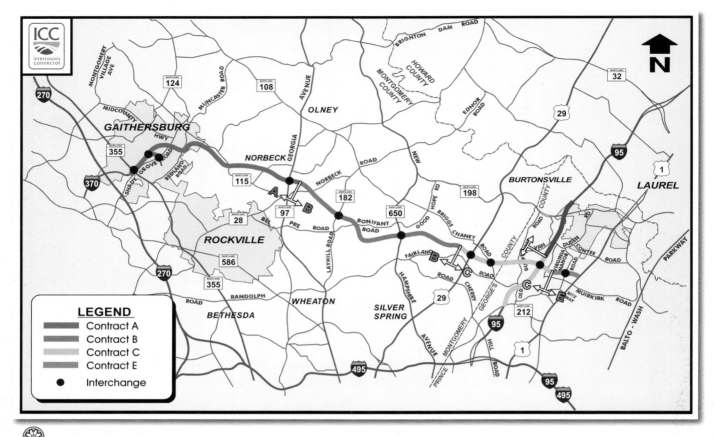

The final piece of the Baltimore-Washington Transportation Grid is an 18.8-mile east-west toll highway between Prince George's and Montgomery counties. The Intercounty Connector was divided into multiple contracts and is expected to be complete in late 2011.

SHA is spending $370 million to mitigate the environmental impact of the ICC, and also to make non-ICC related environmental improvements in areas around the highway. That's $270 million more than required. "Building a new highway or upgrading an old one isn't gentle on the environment," said Raja Veeramachaneni, who was SHA Director of Planning and Preliminary Engineering when the ICC was approved, "but when we go beyond mitigating damage caused by construction and improve the environment in ways that would not have happened otherwise, we expand SHA's role from that of a good steward to a community benefactor as well."

A notable component in the Baltimore-Washington Transportation Grid is the use of heavy rail. Between Baltimore and Washington, the MARC Camden Line (shown above) provides a convenient way to commute from city to city. From Perryville in northeastern Maryland, the MARC Penn Line also travels to Baltimore and D.C. Farther to the west, MARC offers service on the Brunswick Line from Martinsburg, West Virginia and from Frederick, Maryland to Union Station, Washington, D.C. The photo above features a transfer point from MARC to Light Rail at Oriole Park at Camden Yards.

The Baltimore-Washington area continues to expand its reach. Recent years have shown continued growth west beyond Frederick to Hagerstown. In Southern Maryland, commuters to Washington, D.C. and its Virginia suburbs come from Maryland's Calvert, Charles and St. Mary's counties. Two major roads serving Southern Maryland include MD 4 and MD 5. The photo at right depicts MD 5 in Prince George's County about 1951 from Branch Avenue looking east. The modern photo (far right) also shows a section of MD 5 in Prince George's County where MD 5 intersects with Coventry Way.

The Baltimore-Washington Transportation Grid was based on the premise that an automobile-centered society was here to stay. If so, then strategies to change the way Marylanders used their automobiles seemed promising. These strategies, called Transportation Systems Management (TSM), included the construction of park and ride lots, freeway ramps into rail transit parking areas, special high-occupancy vehicle lanes (HOV lanes) for vehicles with multiple riders, and peak-hour bus lanes on upgraded shoulders built to handle traffic.

In the modern era, building highways takes a lot of time. When the planning time stretches over decades, the highway isn't just a road, it's a trip through public policy history. The construction of an east-west "Intercounty Connector" across Montgomery and Prince George's counties is an example.

Plans to connect highways in Montgomery and Prince George's counties began in the 50s as a section of a more ambitious second-level "outer" beltway around Washington, D.C. An outer beltway circling the Capital Beltway (I-495) was a visionary concept in anticipating suburban growth; but no matter how prescient, the "outer" beltway idea withered away for lack of support, with the exception of one part that clung tenaciously to life.

Suburban growth overwhelmed state and county roads in Montgomery and Prince George's counties. Capital Beltway mileage running through those counties became the tightest part of a noose that choked circulation around Washington, D.C. However, environmental-protection legislation made building a new highway a long and tedious process.

When interstate highways were built in the 50s and early 60s, there was no requirement to consider the environment. However, by the 70s and 80s, when local roads in the Washington suburbs became increasingly unsafe and congested, all federally funded construction projects had to prepare an environmental impact statement that met National Environmental Policy Act requirements, including alternative ways to fulfill the project's purpose and need as well as a plan to mitigate any negative environmental consequences that could not be avoided.

The Endangered Species Act of 1973 not only protected fish, wildlife and plants, but also the habitats that supported them. The areas least inhabited by humans, areas that highway planners traditionally favored for new highways, were the most protected by federal environmental legislation. That meant taking the homes of suburban residents for a highway right-of-way. The conundrum surrounding an expressway between Mongomery and Prince George's counties was that the only thing worse than building it was not building it.

Maryland's first Republican governor since Spiro Agnew, Robert L. Ehrlich, Jr., pledged to build the Intercounty Connector (ICC) during his successful election campaign in 2002. When elected, Ehrlich tasked his Secretary of Transportation Robert L. Flanagan with preparing the required environmental impact statements. That was a daunting task because twice before, in 1983 and 1997, the U.S. Environmental Protection Agency and other state environmental agencies had opposed proposed routes due to environmental concerns. Nevertheless, by the end of an 18-month process, the SHA had produced highway plans that met federal requirements. In 2006, the ICC was approved for construction by the Federal Highway Administration.

In the modern era, meeting environmental protection standards isn't the last obstacle to building an expressway. Many major projects — like I-68, I-270, the Naval Academy Bridge and the Woodrow Wilson Bridge — required a day in court. The ICC was no different. In 2007, a U.S. District Court rejected lawsuits filed by environmentalists and some residents who lived along the ICC corridor. The conclusion of a 106-page opinion was that the SHA "went back to the drawing board … and thoroughly considered, examined, and, most importantly, corrected the deficiencies from previous failed attempts."

The ICC will be a six lane, 18.8 mile toll road, connecting Interstate 270 in Montgomery County with the Interstate 95/U.S. 1 corridor in Prince George's County. It will avoid most critical wildlife habitats, but required the purchase of 58 homes. The ICC will also use bridges and storm water runoff technology to minimize the environmental impact. For every acre of parkland affected, SHA will purchase eight new acres elsewhere. When completed in 2011, the ICC will be the most studied, most debated, most environmentally friendly and, at $2.4 billion, one of the costliest highways ever built in Maryland.

As highways became larger and more complex, the tools engineers used to design them also became increasingly high tech. The debut of the personal computer and its full integration into offices in the late 1980s revolutionized the engineering profession.

 Mark Coblentz inhabits a humble studio setting in SHA's District 3 special projects design section, 1978.

DRAFTING BOARDS TO PERSONAL *Computers*

 There were no electronic calculators or computer programs in the early years. This photo shows a slide rule from 1928.

Need to move some dirt? For many years these handy planimeters aided engineers and draftsmen to calculate how much dirt needed to move from one section of road to another. When assembled, the planimeter could trace the outline of a hill or the void in a ravine, and an engineer could find the proper balance for a road grade.

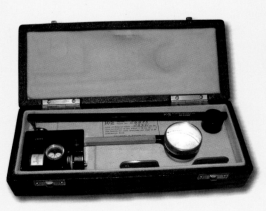

The drafting room at J. E. Greiner shows the typical layout for engineers and draftsmen before the 1980s and the beginning of the computer revolution. Technicians work at drafting tables and review plans on layout tables located behind their chairs. Similar, but perhaps less stylish arrangements, could be found within the SRC and SHA offices.

While mainframe computers came to the agency in the 1950s, the advent of the personal computer revolutionized engineering offices and the skill set required for engineers and drafters. Here, a group of SHA employees in Western Maryland receives training at Allegany Community College, now known as Allegany College of Maryland in Cumberland.

Seated left to right: Typist Clerk III Patty Grove, Office Secretary Bobbie Jean Mihailovich, Sketch Book Reviewer Nevin Bittner and Construction Inspection Division Inspector Gary Sween. Standing left to right: Allegany College Instructor Terry Snyder, Traffic Engineer William Jewell, and Administrative Chief Rev. Jim Bluebaugh.

Chief of Electronic Processing Philip Miller checks some wiring in the SRC's mainframe computer, circa 1954. Miller used this hefty UNIVAC 120 to compile traffic figures and determine material quantities.

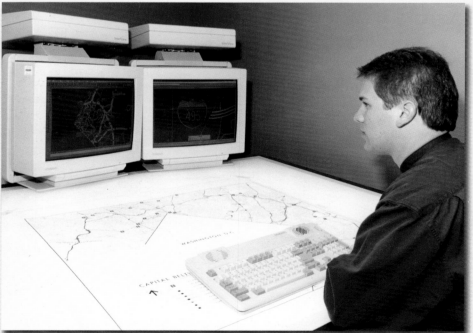

By the late 1980s, plans that had once been inked and lettered could be produced in much less time with computer drafting programs. The days of the open drafting room would soon give way to the office pod.

Sideling Hill

Sideling Hill exposes 350 million years of Maryland history dating back to the coal-forming Mississippian Period of the Paleozoic era. The syncline, a downward folding curve of rock, occurred when the North American and African continents collided about 230 million years ago.

For all of its unintended consequences, the mainstay of Maryland transportation in the modern era has been the interstate. However, a route over the Appalachians, linking Maryland with the Midwest, was late to the Interstate Highway System, despite its rich history of roads, railroads and canals.

Not until the 90s did this historic east-west passage enter the age of interstate highways with the construction of I-68. Opened in 1991, I-68 is an example of the type of technical prowess that made interstates the best-engineered roads in the world.

Economic development was the reason for building I-68. Congress created the Appalachian Regional Commission to encourage economic development, and building a modern interstate through the western Maryland panhandle into West Virginia was an obvious choice. Cumberland, the largest city in the area, was one of only a few metropolitan areas in the country not served by an interstate. Additionally, both Allegany and Garrett counties were "economically distressed jurisdictions" eligible for state tax credits for business relocation, if the businesses could get there.

However, what makes I-68 more than an average interstate wasn't the economic development that it brought to western Maryland; it was the road cut through Sideling Hill, west of Hancock, in Washington County. Sideling Hill was the reason that the National Road (U.S. 40) required travelers to move two miles to the south to pass through the mountains.

To meet interstate standards for I-68, bypassing Sideling Hill wasn't an option. Either a tunnel or a massive mountain cut was required. The cut option was chosen, even though the resulting man-made mountain pass required the removal of 4.75 million cubic yards of soil and rock to create a road cut 340 feet deep from the ridge crest to road level. As with the Chesapeake Bay Bridge, the Sideling Hill Cut provided an extraordinary engineering solution to a historic natural obstacle to travel and commerce.

THE *Underground* RAINBOW

❀ The Sideling Hill cut reveals richly colored layers of sandstone, siltstone, shale, coal and conglomerates in red, maroon, gray, tan, black and white.

❀ Planning for Sideling Hill began in the 1970s while Harry R. Hughes was still Secretary of Transportation. "There was a big issue with Sideling Hill," he says, "which starts at the Potomac and runs all the way up to Pennsylvania. You had to either go over it or around it." Reflecting on the importance of proactive public communication, Hughes adds, "We finally made a decision to make a cut. It was going to be a large cut. We thought environmentalists were going to come out of the woods, but they didn't."

On August 15, 1985 Hughes presided over the opening day celebration for the cut as Governor of Maryland. Left to right, SHA Administrator Hal Kassoff, Mayor of Cumberland George M. Wyckoff, Jr., Maryland Delegate Casper R. Taylor Jr., Governor Harry R. Hughes, State Comptroller Louis Goldstein, unknown, Washington County Delegate Donald F. Munson, Washington County Senator Victor Cushwa and Garrett County Commissioner Ernie Gregg.

Before SHA cut into the mountain, there was some concern among SHA planners about what the mountain would look like. Former SHA geologist Dave Martin said he took borings and presented a technical sketch at a planning meeting. Despite the sketch, no one at the meeting could picture the syncline. Martin had an idea and spoke up, "It's shaped like an upside-down rainbow." Director of Project Planning Fred Gottemoeller responded, "We've got a rainbow!" At that point, Martin says, "they didn't have any problem."

 SHA officials told local residents who attended public meetings that the road cut would be 340-feet deep with benches at 80-foot intervals. Former SHA geologist Dave Martin explains, "People thought there were going to be park benches. There was a casual impression that there would be places to sit. Protesters showed up at the ribbon cutting with signs that asked, 'Where are the benches?'"

Martin explained that the benches were the stepped-back cuts designed to catch loose rock, but afterwards residents continued to request a place to stop and examine the syncline. Local officials, SHA, the Department of Natural Resources and the Maryland Department of Economic and Community Development responded by agreeing to build the Sideling Hill Exhibit Center, a place where travelers can enjoy and learn about Western Maryland geology.

 Six years after the opening of Sideling Hill, the Sideling Hill Exhibit Center opened on August 2, 1991. Inside, visitors study the hill's 350-million year history. Outside, they can take a walk and view that history up close.

 The Sideling Hill Exhibit Center celebrated its one millionth visitor on July 2, 1993. The center affords the opportunity to learn about one of the most interesting exposed rock formations in the northeastern United States.

 A portion of the completed missing link, three to four miles east of Cumberland. In total, Maryland's portion of the National Freeway runs 82 miles from Hancock, Maryland, to the West Virginia border. The total cost for the project was $188 million.

COMPLETING THE *National Freeway*

Despite the completion of Sideling Hill by the mid-1980s, 19.1 miles of National Freeway had yet to be upgraded to freeway standards. Some Western Marylanders wondered if it would ever be finished. Throughout the 1960s and 70s, the federal government offered 70/30 matching funds for Appalachian highways through its Appalachian Development Highway program. But a tightening in government programs during President Reagan's administration put Maryland lawmakers on notice. If the National Freeway was to be finished, they would have to take the lead. Money wasn't the only issue. A portion of the highway was slated to run through a state park, and environmentalists delayed the project with lawsuits.

MDOT Secretary Bill Hellmann came up with a way to make it happen. To find the needed funds, Hellmann eliminated a proposed busway between Baltimore City and County. He also had the Maryland Transportation Authority build the Canton Seagirt Marine Terminal. This freed up money not only to finish the National Freeway but also to build a much needed bridge in Vienna on the Eastern Shore. "What was the most fun," says Hellmann, "was that we called Cas Taylor, who was the leader of the Western Maryland delegation, and said we'd like to meet. So we brought them in along with the Eastern Shore delegation. They didn't suspect anything. And we laid this whole plan out in front of them. It was a nice way to start your term as secretary because all of a sudden you had a lot of friends."

 Pictured at left in this photo, Bill Hellmann recounts the factors that went into the decision to complete the National Freeway. "We went on a bus tour," says Hellmann, "and they showed me the road and I thought, you know, it's sort of their turn. The Baltimore-Washington region had freeways. Why shouldn't Western Maryland finish theirs? Why should Cumberland be isolated by that 20 miles of roadway?"

Left to right, MDOT's Bill Hellmann, SHA District 6 Bill Parks, Hal Kassoff, Ballard Company Wilson Ballard, MDOT Missy Drissel, FHWA Emil Elinsky, SHA District 6 Bob Murray, Ballard Company Ron Rye, RK&K Bob Seitz, SHA Director of Planning and Preliminary Engineering Neil Pedersen, SHA District 6 Wally Beaulieu, RK&K David Wallace, June 1985.

ON THE *Shoulders* OF *Giants*

In the history of Maryland highways, there are three names that run like a thread through the modern era. These are the names of men who found themselves in a unique time and place, and through their sheer grit and determination forced an impression on the road building culture that has lasted to the present day.

By the late 1970s, Maryland's highway builders had taken unprecedented body punches — Spiro Agnew's cash kickbacks from highway consultants, negative press from "road wars" in Baltimore and unprecedented environmental regulations — and it was starting to show in low morale.

This was the environment that M. Slade Caltrider inherited in 1978, when he became SHA Administrator. He was the first head of SHA to work his way up through the ranks, the ultimate company man. He knew how highways were built and maintained, not through studying but through doing. Since leaving the Navy in 1948, he'd worked with survey, maintenance and construction crews. He seemed to have concrete and asphalt in his DNA.

Procedures and protocols were his forte. Slade Caltrider knew how to push jobs through. He brought in his staff for quarterly meetings dedicated to the question: "Is this on schedule?" Projects got on schedule. A dismal capital project completion rate began to improve and so did morale. Caltrider is credited with bringing accountability to Maryland road building, but what he really did was to bring something back, something that had gotten lost — self-confidence.

If the Caltrider years were a time of regrouping, then the other end of the spectrum is the Kassoff years, when Maryland ascended to the ranks of leadership in the national highway community. Hal Kassoff left his mark on Maryland highways as the longest-serving administrator in SHA history, from the mid-80s to the mid-90s, but he was much more than that. He was a visionary, the likes of which Maryland had not seen since Henry Shirley dreamt of a national highway system.

Kassoff's dream was how to make a state highway system work seamlessly. He found answers in technology — like a high-tech Operations Center that provided the nation's first statewide real-time traffic and incident-management capability — and he encouraged Maryland road builders to be bold and innovative. Under Kassoff, Maryland's highway builders became leaders in cutting-edge technology.

The third name that runs through Maryland transportation history is synonymous with the advent of the modern era.

Building new highways in the modern era continues, but with community involvement and concern for the environment. There is another difference as well — the role of the federal government.

In the modern era, the federal government mandated what Maryland had already begun, looking at highways as part of a surface transportation mix.

This transportation brew was known in federal government-speak as "ice tea," for the acronym of the Intermodal Surface Transportation Efficiency Act of 1991 (ISTEA), and its successor TEA-21 (1998). The major innovation of the "teas" is the role of the federal government in planning transportation strategies, many as alternatives to automotive travel, that promote energy efficiency and reduce environmental impact.

Starting in the 60s, with the Highway Safety Act of 1966, the federal government expanded its role from funding highways to protecting the people who drove on them. Signed into law in 2005, SAFETEA-LU (Safe, Accountable, Flexible, and Efficient Transportation Equity Act: A Legacy for Users) was the logical evolution of this way of relating to highways. SAFETEA-LU requires states to develop a Strategic Highway Safety Plan (SHSP) or risk a freeze of transportation funds.

M. Slade Caltrider

Hal Kassoff

Bill Hellmann

William K. "Bill" Hellmann's career spans the heady days of building interstates to today's quest to find the funds to maintain them. By the calendar, the apex of Hellmann's career was 1984 - 1987, when he was Maryland's Secretary of Transportation, but beneath the surface there's much more.

Bill Hellmann's name is associated with the completion of Maryland transportation milestones from the mountains (the last section of I-68, the "National Freeway") to the Eastern Shore (the Vienna Bypass and bridge over the Nanticoke River), and Baltimore's Harbor (the Fort McHenry Tunnel and the Seagirt Marine Terminal) in between.

The projects were impressive, but Hellmann's acumen in getting them funded in ways acceptable to Maryland's General Assembly remains his special gift. With a massively expensive project, the Fort McHenry Tunnel, he negotiated an exception to the federal interstate funding formula that allowed Maryland to finance its share of the cost with revenue bonds backed by tolls collected from the users of the tunnel. He artfully selected an alignment for I-68 that followed the existing U.S. 40 corridor and avoided costly litigation that would have come with other plans, and he used newly granted interstate funding transfer authority in creative ways that provided funding for both the National Freeway and the Vienna Bypass.

In the modern era, Bill Hellmann's voice is what the General Assembly heard when it was asked to increase funding for transportation preservation as well as expansion, and it spoke of revenue sources that legislators could support. Consequently, Maryland's infrastructure avoided the deterioration that some states experienced, and Hellmann became a trusted transportation policy advisor to governors and secretaries of transportation of both political parties.

The leaders of modern Maryland transportation left signature impressions specific to their times, but the fusion of Caltrider's professionalism, Kassoff's vision and Hellmann's know-how left a legacy greater than its constituent parts. The legacy is a corporate culture that values these attributes, and thereby stands on the shoulders of giants.

Maryland's Strategic Highway Safety Plan (SHSP) is built around four E's — engineering, education, enforcement and emergency medical services (EMS), but it's the accountability factor that makes an SHSP more than clever alliteration. SAFETEA-LU requires states to analyze quantitative crash data. The data analysis process is what identifies a state's safety needs, and thereby its safety priorities.

Given the fact that more people lose their lives on Maryland highways than from terrorism, homicide, plane crashes and war, the arrival of a mandated national safety program is a welcome development, but not without a certain irony.

In a sense, federal mandates tied to transportation money have turned the traditional state/federal road building partnership on its head. A voice from the past, Governor Albert Ritchie, asked where was the added value when the federal government "aided" the states by taking taxes from their citizens and gave it back as road aid? The modern era has produced an answer to that question. The added value is in creating national standards for energy efficiency, environmental protection and highway safety by tying federal guidelines to federal-aid funding.

A new process in decision making...

The modern approach to the public meeting process is far different from that practiced in the 1960s and the 1970s. The speaker-audience relationship has been supplemented by more opportunities for SHA representatives and community residents to engage in small group discussions.

CHAPTER 10

A Symphony of Voices

There is much to be said on behalf of the Progressive movement of the first decades of the 20th century, not the least of which was its use of government agencies to make the lives of average Americans better.

The State Roads Commission (SRC) was one of those turn-of-the-twentieth-century agencies rooted in a shared Progressive assumption: that mankind has the ability to control natural forces and impose order upon them.

The SRC also walked on the Achilles' heel characteristic of the Progressives —

the arrogance of good intentions. One veteran of Maryland's road-building past commented that "there was a sense among the professionals in the highway community that we knew best. We were the planners and engineers who knew what it took to build modern highways. It was kind of a patronizing approach, if you want to be candid about it."

When Dennis German began his career as an employee of the Interstate Division for Baltimore City, the credibility of planners and engineers with city residents had been badly shaken by the "road wars" that had roiled local politics in the 1960s.

 When the Interstate Division of Baltimore began restoring streets that passed through ethnic neighborhoods such as Little Italy, Fells Point, and Canton in the 1980s, many of the ideas inherent in such restorations were passed on to SHA. Here on Thames Street, road workers lay Belgian block much like their predecessors would have 100 years before.

In preparation for interstate highway spurs, homes and properties had been condemned on Eastern Avenue and Fleet Street, which ran through Little Italy, and the Boston Street corridor in Canton, where large numbers of Eastern European immigrants had settled and their descendents still lived. The plans for the highways were abandoned in the 1970s. It was Dennis German's job to re-establish the credibility that had been lost. But first he had to convince skeptical residents that he wanted to preserve the character of Baltimore's ethnic neighborhoods.

At community meetings, German and other highway designers proposed brick crosswalks, verandas along the sidewalks, and various amenities that would add to the character of the streets. The residents were encouraged to take an active role in planning changes to their neighborhoods, something sadly lacking before, and together, planners and neighbors agreed on what they liked.

When the Interstate Division for Baltimore City was dissolved, German was transferred to the State Highway Administration (SHA), the road-building successor of the State Roads Commission.

His work with community residents would be a precedent for the future.

The future happened very quickly. The SHA planned to widen a road through Westminster, an important site in Civil War history, and the project would eliminate many old and majestic street trees as well. Community activists were not happy with the project, but fortunately they found a sympathetic ear in then Secretary of Transportation, O. James "Jim" Lighthizer, a Civil War buff, and in an SHA anxious to avoid Baltimore style "road wars."

A task force was formed that included members of the community along with landscape architects, planners and a historian. One of the group's members was Dan Uebersax from SHA's Office of Environmental Design. Uebersax recalls that the group worked together for a year to devise a plan that would save as many of the old trees as possible. The resulting plan restricted the speed of travel by bumping out the sidewalks and providing additional street parking. Brick crosswalks softened the expanse of asphalt and added safety features. Slowing the pace of traffic through town made life more pleasant for residents, and heavy vehicle traffic was directed to a bypass.

The Westminster project demonstrated that highway designers could create attractive roads if they listened to the community and tried to build consensus along the way. The process was lengthy, but SHA was willing to try something new, Uebersax recalled. "It's difficult to do public projects when you come to the end and discover that you haven't made the public happy. In Westminster, SHA created a lot of good-will."

SHA Administrator Parker F. Williams wanted to spread the word about partnering with the community. In 1998, SHA, along with the Federal Highway Administration and the American Association of State Highway and Transportation Officials (AASHTO), hosted a national workshop touting this new approach to building roads in towns and cities. The conference was called "Thinking Beyond the Pavement," and it attracted engineers, designers and planners from 29 state departments of transportation and a variety of others from the federal government, private industry and community organizations.

Main St. WESTMINSTER

 When SHA planned to widen Main Street, MD 32, in Westminster, community activist Rebecca Orenstein alerted her neighbors and had them tie black ribbons around the street trees. She also took her concerns to MDOT Secretary O. James Lighthizer. After the Secretary paid a visit and looked at what might be lost, he charged SHA Administrator Hal Kassoff to take a second look.

Civil War enthusiast and history buff, MDOT Secretary O. James Lighthizer decided that Main Street through Westminster had a character worth preserving. He asked SHA Administrator Hal Kassoff to listen to the local citizens and develop a project that in many ways put pedestrians first. Lighthizer is also remembered as a Secretary who used federal ISTEA legislation and its transportation enhancement funds to purchase historic viewsheds and establish walking trails where railbeds had once traversed the state.

Former Director of SHA's Office of Environmental Design Charles Adams led the task force that developed a new plan for Westminster's Main Street. The result was a redesign for the historic town that provided parking, slowed traffic, and saved trees. But there was more. The multi-disciplinary team of architects, landscape architects, highway engineers, historians and planners pointed the way to a new process, emphasizing more input from community members.

Thinking Beyond THE PAVEMENT

Based on experiences like that in Westminster as well as Governor Parris N. Glendening's new emphasis on Smart Growth, SHA ended the greatest century of road building on record with a conference entitled, "Thinking Beyond the Pavement." Three hundred and twenty-five federal, state and local highway leaders came to Maryland for the two-day workshop. The talk was less about roads than about how those who design them can engage and serve those who live beside them.

"In the pioneering case studies featured at 'Thinking Beyond the Pavement,' we were looking at good projects," said SHA's Director of Environmental Design Charles Adams, "projects that succeeded at making the highway design sensitive to the context in which it was located. But there were ways in which each could have been better still. When we reach the point where all transportation professionals, through this new, collaborative way to design, are open to sharing the full range of their expertise, we will be able to do so much more than we can even now imagine."

SHA Administrator Parker F. Williams speaks at the national workshop, "Thinking Beyond the Pavement," in May, 1998. "I challenge you to help define a process," said Williams, "which will lead to excellence, which produces a project that is carefully, imaginatively designed, serves traffic demand, provides safety for our customers, respects the natural and man-made environments, is viewed as an asset to those who use it, and whose design has the input of professionals and customers alike."

The same year that he presided over the "Thinking Beyond the Pavement" conferece, MDOT Secretary David Winstead followed in the footsteps of Henry Shirley when he became President of the American Association of State Highway and Transportation Officials (AASHTO). That leadership position allowed him to give testimony when Congress renewed the federal ISTEA commitment to multi-modal transportation, by enacting the Transportation Equity Act for the 21st Century (TEA-21).

In 2002, SHA completed *When Main Street is a State Highway*, crystallizing its approach to a multi-disciplinary design process.

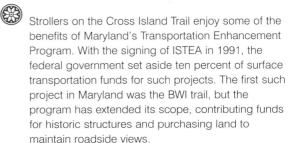 Strollers on the Cross Island Trail enjoy some of the benefits of Maryland's Transportation Enhancement Program. With the signing of ISTEA in 1991, the federal government set aside ten percent of surface transportation funds for such projects. The first such project in Maryland was the BWI trail, but the program has extended its scope, contributing funds for historic structures and purchasing land to maintain roadside views.

Transportation Enhancement Program Coordinator Mary Keller is perhaps most proud of the Oakland B&O station project. Rehabilitation of the station sparked development in the surrounding area and received a Smart Growth award from Governor Parris N. Glendening.

The North Beach Baywalk illustrates another enhancement project that accomplishes the goals of ISTEA and its successors, TEA-21 and SAFETEA-LU. The 1.25-mile long walkway incorporates observation areas that extend over adjoining wetlands. Since 1991, the hallmarks of TEA legislation have been increased mobility, protection of the environment, community preservation, sustainability and livability.

"Thinking Beyond the Pavement" established Maryland as the originator of what is now called Context Sensitive Solutions (CSS), and, in 2002, an SHA publication, *When Main Street is a State Highway,* won the AASHTO President's Transportation Award for Planning.

CSS wasn't just about people driving vehicles. It was about access for pedestrians too. That provided the opportunity to meet other priorities, like access for those with mobility issues as required under the Americans with Disabilities Act of 1990, by constructing sidewalks with curb-ramps. CSS was a new way of looking at urban highways — viewing streets within the context of the town, not simply as a means of moving cars through town — and that was a long way from the "road wars" thinking of the 1960s.

A veteran of the transition from the days of the SRC to the modern era, former Secretary of Transportation Bill Hellmann, could see the difference between then and now. "Once upon a time the hardest part was construction,"

he reflected. "Today, when you get to construction, it's over. It's just a matter of putting the pedal to the metal and building the project. You spend more money in project planning, but you get a better product." The current SHA Administrator Neil J. Pedersen agrees. "We learned over time," he said, "that we should involve the public in every phase of planning and building highways."

Getting the public involved in building highways makes sense, but what if there are two publics? The widening of MD 235, from four lanes to six lanes, offered just that paradox. The project was a stretch of highway that runs between the Patuxent Naval Air Station and the southern Maryland community of Lexington Park.

"In the old days," Pedersen recalled, "that would just be considered a standard suburban arterial road." Only by getting the community involved did the highway planners and engineers discover that widening MD 235 was going to be anything but standard.

There were two ways to widen MD 235: take several local businesses on one side of the road, or two Naval Station buildings on the other. At first glance, it would seem that Lexington Park's "people factor" was the strong suit, but the two Naval Station buildings were eligible for inclusion on the National Register of Historic Places. What followed next is what SHA called "creative mitigation."

"We regrouped," said Pedersen, "and put together a focus group." It included participants from both sides of the highway and the Maryland Historical Trust. What emerged is quite different from the "old days," when the SRC would have built the highway and left the damaged parties to work out financial restitution. The Lexington Park side of the widened highway got landscaping and the Naval Station got a commitment to preserve the memory of the old buildings through exhibits at the Patuxent River Naval Air Museum.

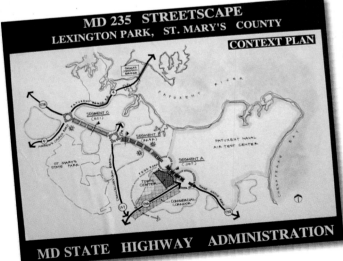

 With a federal base realignment in the 1990s and an influx of people moving to or near the Patuxent Naval Air Station, the old Three Notch Road, MD 235, required additional lanes to accommodate traffic. SHA developed a streetscape along the road that softened impacts while the Naval Air Station enhanced its base with a new museum and outdoor exhibits.

PAX River PROJECT

MDOT Secretary Robert Flanagan (left) and SHA Administrator Neil Pedersen (right). As a planning director under the administrations of Hal Kassoff and Parker F. Williams, Pedersen became expert at developing a planning process that brought multiple stakeholders to the table. For the MD 235 project, he helped negotiate a design that satisfied both local residents and the U.S. Navy. Pedersen was appointed SHA Administrator on May 6, 2003.

This aerial view shows the Patuxent Naval Air Station entrance along with median improvements along MD 235. The naval air museum is at right.

C & O Canal PARKWAY

The C&O Canal Parkway provides residents of Cumberland with increased access to the Cumberland Regional Airport, located in Ridgley, West Virginia. It weaves between the C&O Canal and the existing CSX railroad, providing an exceptional view of Cumberland and the Potomac River. Future plans call for rewatering the canal.

When citizens of Cumberland and SHA wanted to build the C&O Canal Parkway, the National Park Service was opposed. The new parkway might threaten the integrity of the historic canal, shown here with trees on either side between a portion of the parkway and the Potomac River. SHA developed a plan in which a retaining wall would shield the parkway from the canal and expose a portion of the historic waterway previously covered by a flood control levee.

Dealing with structures of historic and environmental value is a fact of life for today's highway planners, but one would be hard pressed to find something with more historic and environmental sensitivity than the Chesapeake and Ohio (C&O) Canal. The C&O Canal was the vision of one president, George Washington, and began in 1828, at a groundbreaking ceremony attended by another one, John Quincy Adams. From 1850 until 1924, the "Grand Old Ditch" operated as a canal running parallel to the Potomac River from Washington, D.C. to Cumberland. In 1971, the canal became the C&O Canal National Historical Park.

Having a national park run through their city was a two-edged sword for Cumberland residents; it was a tourist attraction, but it was also a transportation bottleneck limiting growth in the southern part of the city. Cumberland wanted a two-lane parkway that would weave between the C&O Canal and a railroad yard, extending from the Ford Avenue crossing of the Potomac River to downtown Cumberland.

The proposed parkway was modest in size (only 1.8 miles long) but not in the

A Warren truss bridge over the C&O Canal carries the traditional National Park Service color. The old mule towpath can be seen at left.

baggage that it carried. Back in 1954, the *Washington Post* editorialized in favor of a Blue Ridge Parkway-type road that would run the entire length of the C&O Canal. In an unprecedented turn of events, Supreme Court Justice William O. Douglas lashed out against the idea, saying in a letter to the *Post* that the canal would be "utterly destroyed by a fine two-lane highway." Then he organized a protest hike. The "Immortal Nine," including Douglas, hiked 175 miles along the canal to the delight of

press and wellwishers. The parkway idea was abandoned.

With that kind of background, SHA's commitment to consensus was put to the test. The key stakeholders — including the National Park Service, CSX Transportation, the U.S. Army Corps of Engineers, the City of Cumberland, and the Canal Place Preservation and Development Authority — were brought into the planning process from the beginning, rather than just being presented with a menu of alternatives. What resulted was a highway with the value-added components of a bicycle path and a pedestrian trail, plus a retaining wall that exposed a part of the canal previously covered by a flood control levee.

This enhanced photo envisions future plans for the C&O Canal as a Cumberland tourist attraction. While the rewatered canal will demonstrate 19th century transportation methods, the retaining wall to the right shields the historic site from parkway traffic.

ENVIRONMENTAL *Responsibility*

For the Hampstead bypass project, SHA partnered with the Maryland Department of the Environment to protect the endangered bog turtle. After outfitting the turtles with transmitters, the agencies studied their migration habits and habitat. A management plan was developed to preserve both habitat and turtle. Similarly on the ICC, the agencies identified box turtle habitats and used dogs to sniff out the turtles. They then placed the transponders on the turtles, relocated them and then released them.

The Salisbury Bypass is an example of a good stewardship highway project that minimizes damage to the environment. A portion was built on a bridge to protect the wetlands of the Wicomico River. A temporary wood trestle bridge was used to construct the permanent bridge, eliminating the need to remove tree roots, thus ensuring the re-establishment of vegetation beneath the highway. In recognition of this act of environmental stewardship, SHA received an award from the U.S. Army Corps of Engineers in 2002.

Jersey Heights residents sue to stop bypass

By Dan Kulin
Daily Times Staff Writer

SALISBURY — Residents of a black neighborhood on the city's West Side will go to court to block a planned Route 50 bypass they say would run through their community, bringing pollution and lowering property values.

By choosing the Jersey Heights neighborhood, Maryland perpetuated a long pattern of routing highways in Wicomico County through black neighborhoods, according to residents, a lawsuit filed by a federal neighborhood association and the American Civil Liberties Union.

"I'm satisfied any community in Wicomico County would be doing the same thing if it was happening to them," said Charles Whittington, president of the Jersey Heights Neighborhood Association.

When Route 13 was built in 1942, it went through the black Cuba and Georgetown neighborhoods, and 20 years later when

[Photo caption:] Charles Whittington

Americans have less political power," Hollman said.

Whittington and his neighbors have been fighting against the road going by their homes for more than three years.

"We have talked to almost everybody up to the governor," he said. Whittington has met with representatives from Maryland's State Highway Administration and the state Depart-

When the Salisbury Bypass was scheduled to be built near the homes of African-American residents of Jersey Heights, the residents were upset and took SHA to court. They claimed that a new highway near their neighborhood marked a continuing pattern, a practice of targeting minority communities as locations for new highways. Although SHA had received federal approval for the project and the case's judge found in the agency's favor, SHA, under the leadership of Administrator Parker F. Williams, returned to the community, ready to make changes. The outcome was a revised alignment and improvements to local roads, sparing many hard feelings. *The Daily Times,* Salisbury, September 16, 1997.

The upgrade of U.S. 113 on the Eastern Shore called for a dual roadway to parallel an existing highway from the 1920s that runs through the Coastal Bays Watershed in Worcester County. The Coastal Bays Watershed provides food and shelter for migratory waterfowl and habitat for blue crabs, flounder and clams. It's also home to one very important species of reptile — the diamondback terrapin, the Maryland state reptile and mascot of the University of Maryland. The northern end of the Coastal Bays Watershed is also home to Ocean City, a multi-million-dollar tourist destination, and therein was the challenge of accommodating access without destroying a unique estuary watershed.

Pictured at left is a storm water management pond along a stretch of U.S. 113 north of Berlin. However, even the most aggressive approaches to lessening environmental damage can't change the fact that sometimes wetlands have to be filled, streams crossed and woodlands cut.

The mitigation strategy was to replace lost wetlands with new ones in the same watershed, to change the contours of streambeds while remaining true to the natural tendencies of their flow, and to build "critter crossings" — small bridges and tunnels for animals.

Tourists traveling on U.S. 113 on the way to Ocean City probably don't know it, but they are traveling through one of the most diverse displays of cutting-edge environmental design in the United States. There is even more to the U.S. 113 preservation of environmental assets than meets the eye — a net gain of wetlands. SHA created significantly more wetlands than were required for the project.

SHA won the 2003 Gold Award for the Canal Parkway Project from the National Partnership for Highway Quality (NPHQ). In accepting the award, SHA Administrator Pedersen said, "While we celebrate receipt of the NPHQ award, we're also celebrating the spirit of partnership that brought results and a new beginning for transportation, mobility, development, and historical preservation in Cumberland."

Back in the "old days," partnerships meant presenting a few options that engineers and planners were prepared to build. It was a "pick your poison" approach, former Secretary of Transportation Jim Lighthizer recalled.

Engineers are trained to be "linear thinkers" said Lighthizer. What he meant is that building roads is no longer just engineering, it's about customer service — and that involves peripheral vision, seeing the needs of all of the stakeholders.

Sometimes stakeholders come from very odd places. The planning of the U.S. Naval Academy Bridge involved a stakeholder seldom seen in Maryland road and bridge building — the cultural arts community.

Technically, a "new" upstream Severn River Bridge had already replaced the "old" 1924 Severn River Bridge in 1953. It did its job of moving traffic with six-lane efficiency across the Severn River and it was high enough above the water line that even the tallest ships could pass underneath. However, you wouldn't find the image of the new Severn River Bridge on a postcard, like you would the '24 bridge. The best that could be said of it was that it was functional and offered a spectacular view of the Naval Academy and the Chesapeake Bay.

The two bridges were a classic juxtaposition of form and function. For 40 years, motorists wanting to cross the Severn River in a hurry chose U.S. 50/ U.S. 301 and the "new" bridge; presumably those picking MD 450 and the old bridge found the periodic lifting

THE *Severn River Bridge*

The Severn River Bridge of 1924 began to have trouble in the late 1970s, and SHA did its best to keep the noble structure operational and safe. A new bridge was needed, but the Naval Academy wanted a high bridge, 75 feet of clearance and no bascule, claiming that a high bridge would allow Naval Academy cadets to take out sailboats without interrupting traffic. The residents of Annapolis objected, calling for a mid-level bridge and going so far as to hire a consultant to study the old bridge and to demonstrate how it might be salvaged. Not long after, the counterweight dropped off the old bascule.

The U.S. Naval Academy Bridge, completed in 1994, is as much about art as it is about transportation. Twin box girders, which rest on thin tapered columns with granite covered bases, support the roadway. All that remains of the "old" Severn River Bridge is a 280-foot fishing pier. The demolished parts of the old bridge were removed to form oyster beds. The U.S. Naval Academy Bridge cost $34 million.

The scenic overlook on the bridge allows for expansive views of the Severn River, Annapolis and the Naval Academy.

To choose a design for the new Severn River Bridge, SHA held an international competition, advertising in newspapers and engineering journals. They also assembled a 14-member jury made up of local government officials, state agency representatives and community residents. The jury received tutoring in bridge design, safety and aesthetics and is shown here visiting the 1924 bridge. From the five firms that submitted proposals, the jury chose a design by Greiner Engineering, the Maryland firm that had designed the original bridge.

of the leaf bascules an opportunity to get a bridge-side view of passing boats.

The "old" bridge was more consistent with the historic charm of Annapolis and the Naval Academy than was its upstream neighbor, but boaters complained, including some very important ones at the Naval Academy, about the inconvenience of waiting for the bascules to open and let them pass.

Constant repairs made the '24 bridge a costly price to pay for a scenic drive over the Severn. The decision was made to replace the worn-out bridge. However, at the insistence of Annapolis' most important resident, Governor William Donald Schaefer, the Governor's Office of Art and Culture was assigned a role as a stakeholder in the design of its replacement.

The selection of the design of the replacement bridge was also unusual — a competition with rules developed at public hearings. The jury for what would become the U.S. Naval Academy Bridge was composed of an eclectic group representing cultural, as well as technical, expertise.

No one could remember a bridge designed through a competition, and some engineers must have wondered if being in the customer satisfaction business had gone too far when they read the rule stating that the replacement bridge must be "a work of structural art." Nevertheless, engineering firms throughout the United States and Europe submitted 21 letters of interest; and six were chosen to be finalists. The winner? The Greiner Company (then in the corporate configuration of URS

Greiner, Inc.), which built the original Severn River Bridge in 1924.

In a storybook world, having stakeholder participation and dedication to customer satisfaction would eliminate controversy. In the real world, that doesn't happen. When the decision was made that the replacement bridge would be high enough to let ships pass without a drawbridge, the ugly duckling high-level

bridge upstream came readily to mind. Lots of Annapolitans didn't want another one of those.

SHA's lead bridge engineer, Earle "Jock" Freedman, recalled critics of the replacement bridge hiring their own consultant, who concluded that the '24 bridge had plenty of life left in it, and how Governor Schaefer was concerned that the consultant might be right.

 Celebrations for the opening and dedication of the Naval Academy Bridge, Veterans Day, November, 1994.

SHA employees and engineering consultants trace Maryland's aesthetic bridge movement to Governor William Donald Schaefer. Following his 1987 election, Schaefer appointed Baltimore City Arts Commissioner Jody Albright to see what could be done to improve the appearance of Maryland's buildings and bridges. Albright worked with SHA staff and scheduled the 1988 Bridgescape Conference on Solomon's Island, inviting international bridge experts to answer one simple question, "What makes a beautiful bridge?"

SHA Administrator Hal Kassoff, Governor William Donald Schaefer and Swiss bridge consultant Christian Menn attend the Bridgescape Conference in 1988. Bridge designers from around the world presented papers on railings and piers, lighting and landscaping, texture and proportions. The report that resulted set a new course for SHA with regard to aesthetics and what bridges should look like within a particular context.

The MD 146 Dulaney Valley Road Bridge over the Baltimore Beltway and a former railroad bridge abutment located in the heart of Towson demonstrate the use of themes that can enhance regional identity. Unlike the simple concrete and steel bridge that it replaced, the Dulaney Valley Road Bridge shares a similar stone treatment to historic structures found throughout Towson. A town logo and traditional lighting fixtures further reinforce that theme.

Jock FREEDMAN

Earle S. Freedman, better known to coworkers as "Jock," came to the State Roads Commission in 1950 and first worked on interchanges near the Chesapeake Bay Bridge. Freedman attended Baltimore Polytechnic, as did many of his SRC contemporaries, and later graduated from Johns Hopkins University with a degree in civil engineering. In 1974, he became director of the Office of Bridge Development and has guided that office from the days of building strictly functional bridges to the era of context sensitive design and aesthetics. Freedman names the U.S. Naval Academy Bridge in Annapolis and the restoration of the historic Antietam Bridge at Antietam National Battlefield Park as highlights of his career.

Fifty-plus years at SHA ought to count for something. In December of 2004, it did. One chilly winter day Jock Freedman was asked to visit the recently completed MD 140 Reisterstown Road bridge and meet with elected officials who wanted similar bridges in their districts. When Freedman arrived, he found his family and friends assembled for a dedication ceremony in his honor. Here Freedman stands before the Reisterstown Bridge. Its brick pillars and antique-style lighting fixtures mark SHA's departure from the no-frills steel and concrete designs of the interstate era.

Referred to as an "urban diamond" or "bowtie" among bridge designers, the Reisterstown Road Bridge interchange takes up less land than the traditional cloverleaf while still allowing for a free-flow of traffic.

"I got a marine patrol boat," Freedman said, "and took the governor under the bridge. You could see the reinforcing steel was rusting and exposed and the governor quickly understood what was happening." The argument for salvaging the old bridge sank when a counterweight for the leaf bascules fell off a few days later.

We will never know if those who fought to save the old bridge were satisfied with its replacement, but they must acknowledge that the new U.S. Naval Academy Bridge is an aesthetic next-of-kin to the '24 Severn River Bridge. It has only two lanes with room for sidewalks, like the old bridge, and it has bicycle lanes as well. There are generously placed lamplights, rather than the high glare alternatives, that seem as historic as they are functional, bricks lining parapet

walls in keeping with Annapolis' federal style architecture and a white concrete and steel façade that echoes the light stone buildings of the Naval Academy.

The U.S. Naval Academy Bridge has won its share of awards, including the coveted 1995 Presidential Design Award from the National Endowment for the Arts and the 1996 Federal Highway Administration Award for "Excellence in Highway Design."

The Severn River Bridge competition provided a model for the design of the Woodrow Wilson over the Potomac River. SHA sponsored an open design competition that included the Maryland Department of Transportation, Virginia Department of Transportation, the D.C. Department of Public Works and the Federal Highway Administration. Along with feedback from local communities, the final design reflected a melding of historic Washington D.C. bridges and modern construction aesthetics.

THE *Woodrow Wilson* BRIDGE

The Capital Beltway started with four lanes, and it was progressively widened to eight lanes until the beltway met the Woodrow Wilson Memorial Bridge, which carried traffic over the Potomac River. The Woodrow Wilson had only six lanes, and it had a drawbridge as well.

This was the formula for a classic traffic choke point. Completed in 1961, the Woodrow Wilson Bridge was designed to carry 75,000 vehicles a day. It reached that design capacity in only eight years and when the decision was made to replace it, it was carrying nearly 200,000 vehicles a day.

So common was the Woodrow Wilson rush hour nightmare that more than 300 commuters entered the bridge's "Toughest Bridge Commute Contest." The winner was the victim of a run-in with a tractor trailer that crushed his hip, but the indignity that separated him from the other contestants was being put in an ambulance that went all of 30 feet before stopping as the Woodrow Wilson raised its drawbridge to let a boat pass. The winner had the honor of pressing the plunger that imploded the old bridge.

THE *Woodrow Wilson* BRIDGE

 The alternatives to the Woodrow Wilson were a tunnel, a new bridge with a vertical clearance sufficient to eliminate a draw span and a taller and wider drawbridge. The tunnel was too costly, the high vertical clearance bridge too unsightly and so the new bridge became a drawbridge too, but not your Camelot-era drawbridge. The new Woodrow Wilson Memorial Bridge is actually side-by-side twin drawbridges, the largest moveable bridge in the world, accommodating 10 lanes of traffic. Pictured at left is the old Woodrow Wilson Bridge and construction of the new one.

 At 12:33 a.m. on August 29, 2006, the demolition of a one-half mile section of structural steel beams signaled the end of the old Woodrow Wilson Bridge.

SHA Project Director for the Woodrow Wilson Bridge, Bob Douglass. Originally an employee of the Interstate Division of Baltimore, Douglass came to SHA in 1989, completing the National Freeway's "Missing Link" and a major reconstruction of I-270. In an era when projects can spend many years in the planning stage, Douglass enjoys seeing them finished. "I'm in the project delivery area," he says. "Once we make a decision of what we are going to do, I want to be on the end of the delivery. I go to a lot of meetings, but it's always in the context of how we are going to deliver the project." In 2008, he retired after the second Woodrow Wilson Bridge was complete.

The Woodrow Wilson Bridge incorporates bicycle and pedestrian paths, possible future transit and an observation deck as part of the Potomac Heritage Trail. The deck-over shown here will be the site of interpretive panels that highlight the natural features of the local area and the cultural history of Prince George's County.

Further mitigation efforts for the Woodrow Wilson Bridge project involve restoring 23 acres of tidal wetlands along the Anacostia River near Washington, D.C. It's the largest wetland restoration that SHA has ever attempted and includes nearly six acres of former waste landfill. The project is located in Prince George's County on property owned by the Maryland National Capital Park and Planning Commission.

As part of the Woodrow Wilson Bridge project, the "fish passage program" removed obstacles and artfully placed rocks and boulders to create ramps and pools where fish could swim upstream in areas that had been blocked for decades. The opening of new spawning grounds in five urban streams resulted in numerous national awards.

Inspecting BRIDGES

 SHA's Bridge Inspection Department got underway in 1971. Today there are seven two-person SHA inspection crews, as well as additional consultant crews, each responsible for bridges in specific regions of the state. Impetus for the bridge inspection program occurred in 1967, with the collapse of the Silver River Bridge spanning the Ohio River. Three years later, the federal government passed legislation to initiate the National Bridge Inspection Program.

 Over Liberty Reservoir on MD 26, SHA bridge inspectors Art Gladstone (left) and Bruce Jenkins (right) take a ride in the "under bridge inspection vehicle," or "Snooper," for a better look at steel and concrete. Even in the age of ultrasonic diagnostics, the inspector's most important tools are good eyes, good ears and a hammer. "When it's good concrete," says Chief of Bridge Inspection and Remedial Engineering Joe Miller, "you hear ping, ping, ping. When it's bad concrete, thump, thump, thump."

Building highways and bridges with the input of stakeholders means that government agencies don't have a monopoly on what's in the public's best interest. Making contractors and consultants stakeholders is a page from the continuous quality improvement concept that revolutionized private enterprise in the 80s. The SHA version of it is called the Maryland Quality Initiative (MdQI).

In a sense, MdQI is the mirror opposite of "the arrogance of good intentions" that characterized road-building for much of the 20th century. It's based on a humbling admission: no state agency alone is capable of providing the best projects that each community needs and wants — it takes a partnership.

Along this line of thinking, a statewide "Road to Quality" conference was held in 1993. It was time, said SHA Deputy Administrator and Chief Engineer Doug Rose, to move beyond "forums for finger-pointing" to "ongoing dialogue." The result was the creation of a steering committee of five stakeholders: the State Highway Administration, the Federal Highway Administration, the Consulting Engineers Council of Maryland, the Maryland Asphalt Association and the Maryland Highway Contractors Association.

The first initiative of the new group was rewriting the rules, with contractors' input, on how projects were planned and built. The second was expanding the number of stakeholders, and the third was adding subcommittees to facilitate their input.

Today, at the top of a seven – subcommittee pyramid is the MdQI Steering Committee, which has now grown to 10 entities chaired by the SHA Deputy Administrator/Chief Engineer. More than 90 percent of all construction projects pass over its table in one fashion or another. Each project is unique and receives a customized set of partners to bring it to fruition.

Players in this continuous quality model are what one might expect — consultants, engineers, asphalt and concrete manufacturers and state, local and federal agencies. The next step, said Rose, "is more stakeholder involvement."

That will mean expanding the definition of stakeholder to include the voices of all of those who have an interest in transportation — travelers and shippers, businesses and communities, and those concerned with public health, culture, history, the arts and the natural environment. It's a continuous journey to quality that's open to everyone; it's a symphony of voices created out of a cacophony of input.

 District 1 Engineer Donnie Drewer discusses the collapse with engineer Frank Flynn.

 The original Pocomoke River Bridge dated from the 1920s and had seen better days by August 17, 1988.

August 17, 1988, was a typical summer day on Maryland's lower Eastern Shore. The weather was clear and dry, and the water of the Pocomoke River was calm. Then the day became atypical. Two piles helping to support the 275-foot long MD 675 Bridge over the Pocomoke collapsed. An 85-foot section dropped 30 feet into the river.

Fortunately, no one was hurt, but the reason for the collapse was a mystery. A tell-tale clue was found in the collapsed pilings. They were eight inches in circumference when they should have been no less than 12 inches. The culprit was the combined effect of bacteria, fungi, and aquatic insect larvae that had eaten away at the submerged timber piles.

Now bridge inspectors conduct underwater measurements of timber piles and are taught to detect aquatic insect larvae and to analyze bore samples for bacteria, fungi and other contaminants. Bridges using wooden piles to support them are much safer because science used at a disaster site detected a hidden enemy below the waterline.

 The National Partnership for Highway Quality (NPHQ) extends public-private partnership thinking to the national level, bringing highway agencies and private industry together, combining their expertise, and advancing highway quality, safety and service to highway users.

 Reopening the Pocomoke River Bridge in 1989.

 **MdQI**
Maryland Quality Initiative

 The Maryland Quality Initiative adds another group of stakeholders to the road construction mix — consultant and contracting industries.

I-95 TUNNEL
EXPECT CONGESTION
AND DELAYS

Going high-tech...

Traffic control centers in various regions of the state monitor minute-by-minute traffic conditions letting motorists know the best route of travel when roads become congested.

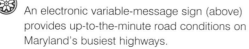 An electronic variable-message sign (above) provides up-to-the-minute road conditions on Maryland's busiest highways.

 The high-tech component of CHART is complemented by courtesy patrol units that move stalled motorists out of harm's way. At right, a courtesy patrolman helps repair a tire until the motorist can seek more comprehensive service.

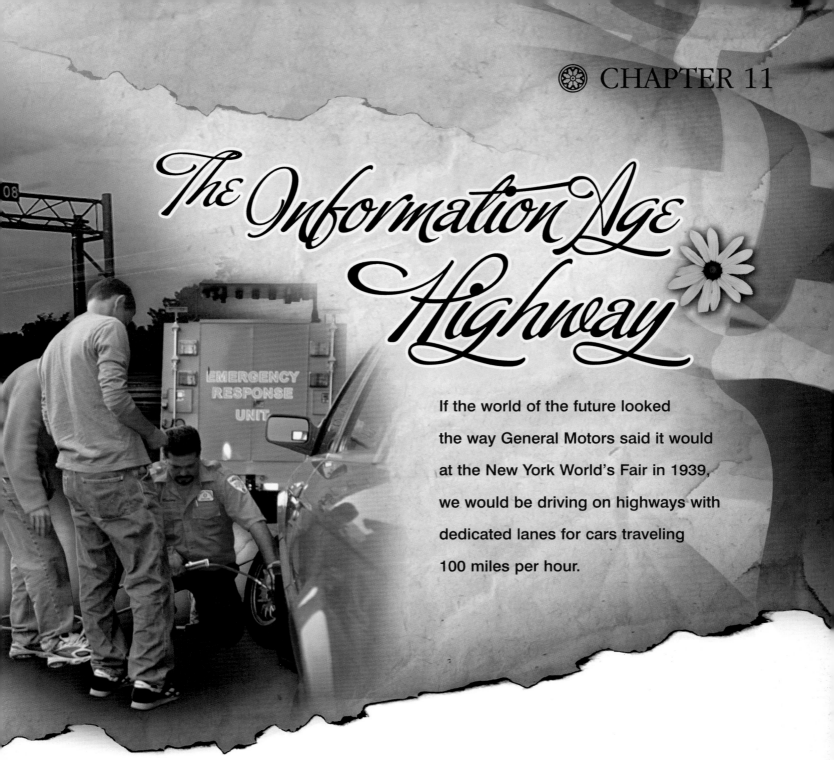

CHAPTER 11

The Information Age Highway

If the world of the future looked the way General Motors said it would at the New York World's Fair in 1939, we would be driving on highways with dedicated lanes for cars traveling 100 miles per hour.

The "Futurama" exhibit got the dedicated lanes right, but not who would be riding on them. They turned out to be high-occupancy vehicle (HOV) lanes for cars with multiple passengers, not speeding motorists.

If Futurama had predicted that Maryland would have an expressway running through a man-made mountain pass, bridges spanning the Chesapeake Bay and tunnels moving people and freight under Baltimore's harbor, the exhibit might have been called the "Golden Age of Tomorrow."

Those engineering wonders would have astounded an audience in 1939.

However, today's commuters stuck in rush-hour traffic on the Washington and Baltimore beltways or beach-bound vacationers waiting to cross the Chesapeake Bay Bridge would be equally astounded if told that they were living in a "Golden Age."

H.L. Mencken GOT IT WRONG

In 1933, when Mencken made that prediction, a ferry system carried 180 cars per hour across the Bay. The opening of the two-lane Chesapeake Bay Bridge in 1952 increased capacity to 1,500 cars per hour and the three lanes of the second span, opened in 1973, increased capacity to 3,750 cars per hour.

Mencken predicted that a bridge over the Chesapeake Bay would never collect enough tolls to pay for its construction, and even state officials estimated that it would take 40 years to collect $45 million in tolls. The William Preston Lane, Jr. Memorial (Bay) Bridge raised $41 million in tolls in just its first 10 years of operation.

In 2007, Maryland joined 10 other states in adopting the California clean air standards. Pending approval by the U.S. Environmental Protection Agency, in 2010 the Clean Cars Act would require a reduction in the average carbon dioxide emissions of cars sold in Maryland. That would mean that cars stuck in traffic congestion would spew less carbon dioxide into the air, but if the traffic flowed smoothly, there would be 44 hours less of carbon dioxide emissions per commuter.

❂ Even the "Sage of Baltimore," H.L. Mencken was caught in present-centered bad prophecy when he argued against a bridge over the Chesapeake Bay, because "there is simply not traffic enough between the Eastern and Western Shores, and there is no evidence that there will ever be enough hereafter."

Clean Air Act

 The 44 hours that the average Baltimore-area commuter spent in 2005 traffic congestion wasn't just about wasted time. It was also about burning 32 extra gallons of fuel and putting carbon dioxide into the air that didn't need to be there. Carbon dioxide is a "greenhouse" gas and a cause of global warming. Automobiles produce a third of the nation's greenhouse gas emissions.

Maryland has come a long way since the State Roads Commission started paving roads to get "farmers out of the mud." But just as clearly, there's a long way yet to go, and no one knows with certainty how we are going to get there.

Forecasting the future is a risky game because of a present-centered predicament: all of our information comes from the present and the past. What we know from the present is the direction that transportation is taking, but not its destination, or what's between here and there.

The conventional wisdom is that Marylanders require an "integrated" mix of transportation modes and methods. A toolbox is often used as a metaphor to explain the concept, with highways being just one tool. If so, it's the busiest tool in the box.

Here is what we know. In spite of a light rail system, a subway, buses, a commuter rail service between Baltimore and Washington, record high gasoline prices, high-occupancy vehicle (HOV) lanes, carpooling, and park and ride convenience, 73.3 percent (19 million) of all commuting Marylanders drive to work alone in their cars. Less than five percent of the national workforce uses mass transit. For most commuters, the modern highway offers something that mass transit can't match — point-to-point convenience.

We know this as well: There is a price to be paid for dependence on automobiles. Between 1982 and 2005, the annual Baltimore-area commuter's lost time in traffic congestion rose from 11 hours to 44 hours, according to the widely followed Urban Mobility Report. The reason is that more Marylanders than

ever are picking automobiles as their preferred mode of transportation. There was a 518,232 increase in the number of licensed drivers and a 909,224 increase in the number of passenger vehicles registered in Maryland between 1996 and 2007.

Did Maryland take farmers out of the mud, only to put urban commuters into traffic jams?

Already the State Highway Administration (SHA) spends approximately 52 percent of its budget on maintaining existing highways. In addition, building new highways and widening existing ones has never been more time consuming and expensive, and BRAC is just around the corner.

BRAC is the acronym for Base Realignment and Closure. It's the process authorized by Congress for reorganizing military bases. The goal is efficiency in support of the armed forces, which means that some military facilities are reduced or closed while others are expanded. Expansion of military bases in Maryland has been part of the recent rounds of the BRAC process.

The latest round of BRAC was announced in 2005 for 2011 implementation. Secretary of Transportation John D. Porcari said that at least MDOT knows "the regions to which people will be moving, the impact and the time frame."

Two of those regions, Aberdeen Proving Ground and Fort George G. Meade, come with lots of challenges. The Aberdeen facility is in Harford County, north of Baltimore, and Ft. Meade is in Anne Arundel County, south of Baltimore. Both Harford and Anne

Arundel counties are already among the fastest growing counties in Maryland.

At Aberdeen, MDOT recommends building an intersection of U.S. 40 with MD 715 and widening I-95, but the former will cost $17 million and the latter over $2 billion. Highway improvements around Fort Meade would cost an additional $1.5 billion. There may be a mass transit ray of hope. Maryland Rail Commuter (MARC) trains serve both the Aberdeen and Fort Meade areas, but additional trains will require the consent of Amtrak and CSX, with whom MARC shares the tracks.

"It is imperative that we stay ahead of the curve," Secretary Porcari told the Maryland Economic Development Association, but that will be a challenge, since there is already a backlog of non-BRAC-related projects in the suburban counties around Baltimore.

The discrepancy between transportation needs and funds isn't just a Maryland phenomenon; all states are facing varying degrees of the same thing. This has led some highway visionaries and political pundits to suggest novel ways of financing new highways — private/public partnerships (PPPs).

PPPs sound like something the local Rotary might be sponsoring, but in fact they are a revolutionary change in how roads are constructed and maintained. An oft-discussed option would have the state provide land rights-of-way and private companies build and manage the highways. Both would share the revenue in tolls. Another private/public option is the sale or long-term lease of existing highways for an up-front payment. This "secularizing" (selling future revenue) would provide an immediate infusion of

Fee-based transportation isn't a new idea, but the failure of private turnpike companies to remain profitable in the 19th century and the decision to pay for interstate highways from a Highway Trust Fund in the 20th century left fee-based transportation on the back burner.

In Maryland, fee-based transportation may have been on the back burner, but the flame never went out because the State Roads Commission used revenue bonds backed by tolls as a way to pay for bridges and tunnels. In 1971, when the Maryland Department of Transportation was created, so was an enterprise agency, the Maryland Transportation Authority (MdTA), which has responsibility for financing, constructing, operating and maintaining revenue-producing transportation projects.

Today, the MdTA operates seven toll facilities — a section of I-95 from Baltimore to Delaware; both Baltimore Harbor tunnels; bridges across the Chesapeake Bay, the Susquehanna River and the Potomac River; and the Francis Scott Key Bridge crossing the

 While the Cumberland Toll House in LaVale may appear to be a relic of the past, toll facilities remain a viable way for the state to build and maintain the roads of the future. Below MdTA Toll Collector Danielle Collins greets Maryland motorists with a smile.

Paying YOUR OWN WAY

Outer Harbor on Baltimore's beltway. In the near future MdTA toll facilities will increase in number, and the Intercounty Connector (ICC) will be a toll-based expressway, in ways not seen before.

In 2005, the MdTA received federal approval to construct Express Toll Lanes (ETLs) on the most congested portion of I-95 north of Baltimore City. A 10-mile segment will have both free general-purpose lanes and ETLs collecting tolls that will vary depending on the amount of traffic on the road.

 E-ZPass is an electronic toll collection system (a prepaid debit account) available at all seven of Maryland's toll collection facilities, as well as toll facilities throughout the northeast. In the future, E-ZPass-type technology could be used to influence transportation choices by factoring in variable-pricing discounts for off-peak hours, or for differential pricing for lane access.

cash and be an alternative to raising fuel taxes and registration fees. The American Automobile Association called these ideas "big pots of money" dangling before the state DOTs, but not everyone is sure that turning over highways to private enterprise is the best choice for Maryland.

A more conservative way to make highways pay for themselves is called "congestion pricing." This works by usingthe same principle that customer service industries employ, differential pricing for access to services. In the case of highways, the value added is special lanes. Lane prices could be posted on electronic signs that continually change to reflect traffic flow. Drivers picking the less congested fee-based lanes would help finance new highways by paying for that convenience, and by abandoning the free lanes, they would help reduce congestion for everyone else.

Some highway planners look for a technology fix, a magic bullet to force out enough productivity from existing highways to avoid building and collecting tolls on new ones. They predict that in the future, Maryland will break up the rolling parking lots of rush hour by using highways more intelligently and thus avoid the need to make a profit from them.

In fact, Intelligent Transportation Systems (ITS) are already here. The electronic toll collection system, E-ZPass, is operational on all Maryland toll roads, bridges and tunnels. There are also electronic variable-message signs and highway-advisory-radio channels giving traffic updates, systemized traffic signals, pavement weather sensors and closed-circuit television cameras reporting breakdowns. These intelligent technologies help drivers get the most out of existing roads and reduce lost time and wasted fuel caused by backups.

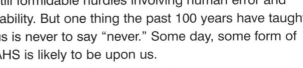

THE ELECTRONIC *Chauffeur*

If airplanes have autopilots, can't automobiles have electronic chauffeurs? Welcome to the world of the Automated Highway System (AHS). On an AHS highway, "smart" cars are equipped with radar, computers and sensing devices that read data embedded in the road. Information passes from road to car and car to road via a central control system that can drive cars in multi-vehicle platoon formations.

The distance between cars in a platoon can be much closer than manual driving would allow, thus increasing the volume of transportation and reducing traffic congestion. Platoons of cars will also be more aerodynamic than individual cars and thus decrease fuel consumption and tailpipe emissions.

Will the AHS happen soon? Perhaps not. There are still formidable hurdles involving human error and liability. But one thing the past 100 years have taught us is never to say "never." Some day, some form of AHS is likely to be upon us.

HOW *Highways* GOT *Smart*

Maryland was an early adopter of Intelligent Transportation Systems (ITS), but its conversion to high-tech transportation didn't begin on the road to Damascus — it came on the road to the beach. At least that's the way former SHA Administrator Hal Kassoff recalls it.

When the Mayor of Baltimore, William Donald Schaefer, was elected governor in 1986, Maryland Transportation Secretary Bill Hellmann and Kassoff were called to his office. "Bill coached me on how to interact with Schaefer," Kassoff remembers, "but when the governor-elect told me he wanted to improve the flow of traffic to Ocean City in six months, I thought I'd better update my resume because there was no way to make hundreds of millions of dollars in capital improvements by June. When we left Schaefer's office I asked Bill, only half joking, if I should think about a career change. Bill's advice was "don't panic, just be creative and come back with a plan that produces some visible improvement. Just make things better in a way that will be noticed."

 A *Reach the Beach* advertisement from 1987, alerting motorists in Washington and Baltimore to the best way to get "Downy Ocean."

 Backups on U.S. 50 continued during *Reach the Beach*, but even in this photo, paved road shoulders demonstrate SHA's efforts to make improvements.

Reach the Beach represented a cooperative effort between SHA, MdTA and the Maryland State Police. "We got motorcycles for the state police," says Hal Kassoff, "so they could penetrate traffic jams. We had helicopters, fixed wing aircraft. We had a sound truck to let people know the traffic conditions downstream. We also had a Beach Bongo bus for mass transportation that they thought younger people would want to ride in. The improvement was modest at first. But people noticed the effort."

The plan that Kassoff presented was the result of "brainstorming" with his SHA traffic engineers, State Police, the Maryland Transportation Authority (which administers the Bay Bridge) and with local officials from the Bay Bridge to Ocean City. It was called *Reach the Beach* and emphasized "real-time" management of the road to the beach, U.S. 50, through teamwork and technology.

Reach the Beach caught on and it made a difference that people noticed. Governor Schaefer showed up for the opening day as a toll collector, to the delight of surprised motorists who found a rare reason to smile about their trip to Ocean City. And over the next few years, SHA delivered a string of new bridges and bypasses that greatly improved the plight of travelers on the Eastern Shore.

Reach the Beach evolved into a statewide traffic management program, called the Chesapeake Highway Advisory Routing Traffic. It was later renamed the Coordinated Highway Action Response Team or "CHART." The backbone of CHART is a computerized system that assists in analyzing traffic information based on highway cameras, speed detectors, roadway weather sensors, and reports from emergency patrol units.

Operators view real-time highway conditions at various locations across the state on a number of video screens. They can provide traveler information via electronic signs, live traffic cameras and real-time traffic maps, and they can dispatch emergency traffic patrols.

Smart highways are efficient highways that reduce transportation costs to highway users, which is a reason for current businesses to want to stay and new ones to come to Maryland. In 2006, CHART was credited with reducing incident delays by 37.5 million vehicle traffic hours.

Starting a traffic management program to serve summer vacationers rather than rush hour commuters may seem like a backward approach. But *Reach the Beach* provided a laboratory to find out what worked. Courtesy patrol trucks modeled on Chicago's "Minutemen" system were employed to push stalled cars off U.S. 50 and keep traffic moving. Patrolmen could then better assist motorists.

 Following the *Reach the Beach* efforts, Director of Traffic and Safety Tom Hicks and Chief Engineer Bob Olsen traveled with SHA Administrator Hal Kassoff to Chicago. The Illinois Department of Transportation had developed what was then called the Chicago Area Surveillance Project, a traffic management program that measured traffic volumes and provided commuters with up-to-the-minute traffic conditions. Kassoff, Hicks and Olsen were sure to draw upon the best intelligent transportation systems then in operation before implementing a full-time system in Maryland.

SHA opened the CHART Operations Center in 1995 and on January 15, 2004, it was re-dedicated as the Hal Kassoff Statewide Operations Center, honoring Kassoff's pioneering efforts in Maryland's program for traffic management. Left to right, MDOT Secretary Robert Flanagan, SHA Administrator Neil Pedersen, son-in-law Alec Kassoff, daughter Debra Kassoff, wife Lori Kassoff, Hal Kassoff and son Jason Kassoff.

THE *Superstorm* OF '93

 Ron Hockman, Edwin Gordon and Dorsey Guard stand in front of an Oshkosh truck mounted with a snow blower, Garrett County.

 Before the storm of '93, SHA assigned snowplows to sections of road; work crews kept those sections clear, plowing all night when necessary. Once CHART was formed, better knowledge of conditions and better communications allowed crews more flexibility, traveling from place to place as information on the most troubled spots became available.

In the Mid-Atlantic region, March is the time of lions turning to lambs in the metaphors used by weather forecasters, but in March of 1993 the lambs were nowhere in sight. On March 12, a nor'easter with wind gusts up to 69-mph blew in from the ocean and buried Baltimore under a foot of snow. Western Maryland fared even worse. Hagerstown received 20 inches of snow and Piney Dam in Garrett County recorded 31 inches and snow drifts up to 12 feet.

The National Weather Service named it the "Superstorm of '93" because of its large area of impact from the Gulf of Mexico to New England. The National Guard was called in, but the frontline for snow removal was State Highway Administration (SHA) and Maryland Transportation Authority (MdTA) workers who valiantly kept highways and bridges open by working around the clock.

One SHA employee, Jim Spears, set a record by working 230 hours removing snow over a two-week period. "We worked either a 12-hour or a 16-hour shift," Spears recalled. "The snow was so bad, we stopped at the Rustic Inn. They let us in there. There were people stranded and they were lying everywhere on the floor. They would cover their heads with a chair so nobody would step on their faces. It was so crowded I went back out, ran the motor and slept in the truck."

Meanwhile, in the Baltimore-Washington area, SHA Administrator Hal Kassoff received a call from FHWA Administrator Rodney Slater. Washington, D.C. needed help with its snow removal, so Kassoff sent trucks into the district. Late that night, Kassoff was out checking Maryland roads when he got a second call from Slater and another D.C dignitary. "It was President Clinton," says Kassoff. "I almost ran off the road. The president said, 'Maybe no one will ever know, but you really helped us out.'"

 Introduction of trucks such as those above marks a clear advance in technology over the past. Fitted with plows on the front and automated salt spreaders or de-icing equipment in the rear, SHA crew members no longer ride in truck beds shoveling salt or cinders onto roads as was once the practice.

Tidy cab interiors among equipment operators are a point of pride, perhaps because they often double as temporary living spaces during harsh storms. With snow shift work extending from 10 to 12 hours and more, drivers often run on adrenaline and may only return to their maintenance shops for a short rest on a portable cot. Then it's time for another shift.

New financing methods may produce more highways and intelligent transportation strategies may reduce traffic congestion, but here is a cautionary tale. By the mid-80s, a 12-mile stretch of I-270 from the Washington Beltway into Montgomery County was the most congested road in Maryland. It was widened to 12 lanes and that relieved traffic congestion, but not for long. It's back — one of the worst commutes in Maryland.

Forecasting the future of highways is a risky game because it's full of wild cards. One of the wild cards is a phenomenon called "induced traffic." Good highways attract drivers from lesser roads, even if the lesser road is a more direct route, because commuters don't measure driving in distance, they measure it in time. Half the time on an expressway trumps half the distance of stop-and-go traffic on local roads.

The challenge in making proactive transportation plans is that transportation is reactive to land-use decisions made by local governments. Changes in zoning that allow for the residential and commercial development of agricultural land increase traffic on existing roads. When roads are widened or new roads are built, it often stimulates more development. In the five years before I-270 got its extra lanes, there were 1,745 new homes approved in the 12 miles north of Rockville. In the five years after the widening of I-270, 13,642 new homes were approved. If this sounds familiar, it's not surprising. Development has been following

"Smart" STARTS WITH Science

More than any other nomenclature, "smart" is the word most likely to dominate highway vocabulary in the future. "Smart" is already a strategy to build roads to new communities, revitalize old communities and make roads interactive with the cars that drive on them.

If a prerequisite for smart roads is scientific testing, then Maryland has been building roads the smart way for a very long time. In fact, there was a materials testing lab in the Maryland Geological Survey before there was a State Roads Commission (SRC).

The lab's early days were spent evaluating the structural integrity of bricks, but soon moved on to asphalt and concrete. An anecdote from those times tells of a vendor reacting to the rejection of his product with indignation. "If we had supposed you were testing materials in Maryland," he replied, "we would have shipped a better product."

Today, using science to make the transportation infrastructure last longer is a priority. Maryland is one of a seven-state team formed by the American Association of

Deborah Lochte tests bridge deck samples for chloride content in SHA's Materials and Testing Lab. Aside from testing concrete and asphalt, the lab also tests paints, reflective material and anything else that might be used in constructing a road.

highways since Crain Highway, the "superhighway" of its day, was built in the 1920s.

The lesson is that traffic congestion is about something more fundamental than transportation. It's about where we live. The 1997 General Assembly, urged on by Governor Parris Glendening, passed five pieces of legislation, which Glendening called "smart growth" laws, to encourage development in Maryland's existing towns, cities, and suburbs or in new Priority Funding Areas (PFAs), which are

county-designated areas where local governments want to direct growth. The thinking was that if Marylanders lived in areas with existing infrastructure like roads, new highways wouldn't be needed. For new development in PFAs, transportation was to be part of the plan.

King Farm in Rockville is an example of smart growth. It's a new community with three times the housing density of Rockville, but its residents have something other than beleaguered I-270 as a transportation option. High-density

apartments and condominiums, as well as commercial spaces, are laid out in a "T" near the Shady Grove Metro Station. Farther out, housing shifts to town homes and single-family detached houses, which are serviced by private shuttle buses making a continuous loop to the Metro. Twenty-four bus routes and the Metro Red Line converge at the Shady Grove Station for mass transit options in the I-270 and I-70 corridors, Montgomery County and most of Washington, D.C.

The ARAN vehicle, pictured at left and driven by Sandra Titus, is actually a rolling laboratory collecting evidence of road conditions.

State Highway and Transportation Officials to test a new emerging technology called "Superpave." It's the first significant innovation in hot asphalt research since World War II.

Superpave (SUperior PERforming Asphalt PAVEments) mixes are designed specifically for a region's climate and driving conditions, often using high-tech materials like polymer-modified binders.

Designer highways may be the future, but in the present, fighting an old enemy, the pothole, is just as important. The pothole is the sign of snow, ice or rain's victory over roads. However, science has now provided a high-tech weapon for road builders. Enter the Automatic Road Analyzer (ARAN) vehicle.

The ARAN vehicle is one of the most advanced platforms in the world for collecting data on the conditions of roads. It provides a historical record of consistent data that is more reliable than the subjective visual inspections of the past. With the ARAN, the secret of taming the destructive effects of water is preventive maintenance, which is less costly than patching a pothole.

The science that supports road construction has come a long way since the days of inspecting bricks, but in some ways there are still echoes from the past. The latest innovation from Germany promises a near permanent road surface. It's called splittmastixasphalt, which translates as stone-matrix asphalt. Beyond the high-tech binders is the physics of stone-on-stone contact, which Maryland used on the first macadam road in the United States, the Cumberland Turnpike. "Maryland has been a leader in using scientific principles to create state-of-the-art highways since the 19th century," said Chief Engineer for Operations and Duputy Administrator Doug Rose. "I don't see why that's going to change in the future."

Smart Growth

Smart Growth legislation signed in 1997 was a way to attack sprawl and attract growth to existing Maryland communities. It may not seem like a giant step, but one of the stipulations affecting SHA concerned sidewalks. Before Smart Growth, SHA could not build sidewalks; after the legislation went into effect, any road project in an urban area had to include new or upgraded sidewalks. The result is that SHA has far more interaction with local communities.

Governor Parris N. Glendening, elected officials and students from North Harford School complex celebrate the opening of the MD 165 pedestrian underpass. Beginning in the 1990s, Glendening and SHA Administrator Parker Williams presided over a new phase in road building, making local residents a much larger component in the design process.

Director of the Community Design Division, Dennis German (center) says that an important element of the new Context Sensitive Design (CSD) approach was making sure that new road designs fit with a town's master plan, in some cases making sure that the town had a plan. For this reason MDOT planner Yolanda Takesian (right) was brought into the CSD process to provide long-term coordination between roadway improvements and community planning. Here Takesian and German listen to Highway Design Division Chief Eric Marabello discuss designs for a new roundabout.

The opening of the Reisterstown streetscape on MD 140 revitalized an existing commercial area and marked the beginning of a new road-building program. Left to right, County Councilman Bryan McIntyre, Delegate Dan Morhaim, Delegate Robert Frank, District 4 Engineer Dave Malkowski, Carolyn Smith, SHA Administrator Parker Williams, David Fields, Senator Paula Hollinger and Delegate Michael Finifter.

The first main street project completed under the Smart Growth initiative was this streetscape for MD 140, Reisterstown Road. The new main street highlights local business, including several antiques stores and boutique shops. Three similar projects were also part of the initial push — MD 211 in Prince George's County, MD 343 in Cambridge and MD 2 in Brooklyn.

Amenities along new streetscapes such as those shown here in Greensboro along MD 314 often include landscaping, narrower roadways, safer turning lanes, pedestrian friendly street lighting, ADA accommodation and brick paving that maintains the historic character of a community.

Streetscapes now span the state, such as this one in Frostburg, Maryland, where landscape elements are integral to roadway design. While the first streetscape projects averaged $1.8 million, more recent efforts have averaged $4 million, and several new ones are up to $8 million. "The Neighborhood Conservation Program," says Dennis German, "is the Cadillac of the preservation system."

Streetscape on MD 222 at Port Deposit. The Neighborhood Conservation Program gave SHA an opportunity to formalize a process that became apparent in Westminster and other projects of the early 90s. Today, the program comprises $200 million out of a $1.1 billion budget.

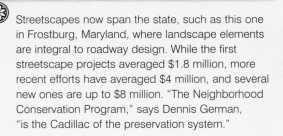

Planned communities aren't new in Maryland. Greenbelt, in Prince George's County, was a New Deal experiment aimed at creating affordable housing and communal living during the Great Depression. Columbia, in Howard County, was opened in 1967 by the pioneering developer James Rouse, who conceived of it as an experiment in eliminating religious, income and race segregation.

Smart Growth is different from the planned communities of Maryland's past because it's less of an experiment in social engineering than a proactive growth philosophy. As such, the role of the Maryland Department of Transportation (MDOT) is factored into land use decisions by directing transportation resources into Priority Funding Areas — those with compact development.

Smart Growth offers the promise of relieving traffic congestion in the long term, but that's little comfort to commuters driving in the here and now. Recent SHA Administrators Parker F. Williams and Neil Pedersen turned to innovative experiments to relieve traffic snarls and make commuting more bearable.

As every commuter knows, the left turn at a busy intersection wastes time and fuel, but short of an expensive and environmentally invasive grade separation, there didn't seem to be an alternative. Don't tell that to commuters at the juncture of MD 228 and MD 210 in Prince George's County. They probably don't know it, but they are driving on the first full-scale continuous flow intersection (CFI) in the United States.

The genius of the CFI is that it moves left-turning traffic into special bays before it reaches the intersection. Then left-turn bay signals, which are computer-coordinated with the intersection traffic lights, move left-turning cars through the intersection on the same green light as through traffic, in a smooth continuous traffic flow. This saves time and gasoline, which is why the intersection of MD highways 228 and 210 won the prestigious Francis B. Francois Award for Innovation from the American Association of State Highway and Transportation Officials in 2002.

Smart Choices

 "Why don't you Americans try roundabouts?" That was the question British engineer Kenneth Todd asked SHA Administrator Hal Kassoff and SHA Director of Traffic and Safety Tom Hicks whenever he visited Maryland. By the time the Lisbon roundabout at MD 94 and MD 144 was completed in 1994, SHA was emerging as a national leader in traffic control.

This continuous flow intersection at MD 228 and MD 210 is actually two closely-spaced intersections timed to operate as one unit. This eliminates conflicting left turns, which reduces the number of required traffic light changes and creates more green light time for commuters.

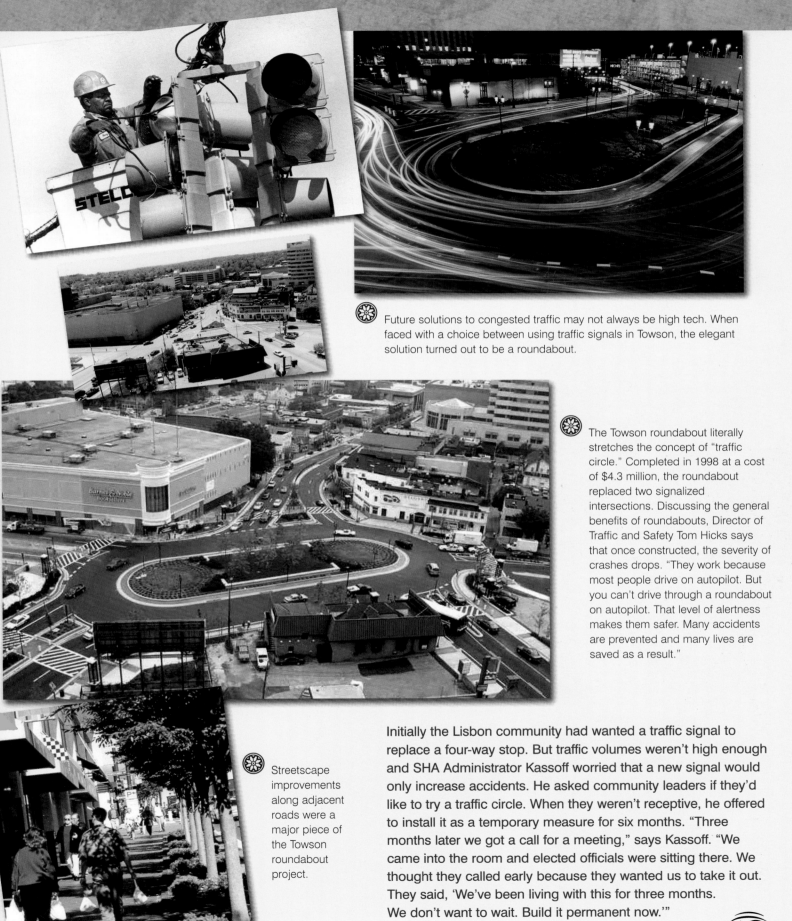

Future solutions to congested traffic may not always be high tech. When faced with a choice between using traffic signals in Towson, the elegant solution turned out to be a roundabout.

The Towson roundabout literally stretches the concept of "traffic circle." Completed in 1998 at a cost of $4.3 million, the roundabout replaced two signalized intersections. Discussing the general benefits of roundabouts, Director of Traffic and Safety Tom Hicks says that once constructed, the severity of crashes drops. "They work because most people drive on autopilot. But you can't drive through a roundabout on autopilot. That level of alertness makes them safer. Many accidents are prevented and many lives are saved as a result."

Streetscape improvements along adjacent roads were a major piece of the Towson roundabout project.

Initially the Lisbon community had wanted a traffic signal to replace a four-way stop. But traffic volumes weren't high enough and SHA Administrator Kassoff worried that a new signal would only increase accidents. He asked community leaders if they'd like to try a traffic circle. When they weren't receptive, he offered to install it as a temporary measure for six months. "Three months later we got a call for a meeting," says Kassoff. "We came into the room and elected officials were sitting there. We thought they called early because they wanted us to take it out. They said, 'We've been living with this for three months. We don't want to wait. Build it permanent now.'"

THE *Other Side* OF HIGH TECH

While Maryland road builders of the future look for new ways to fight congestion and promote more balanced development along highways, some elements of road building remain constant. Anyone with a computer knows that the latest technology is only as smart as the operator, and in many instances there will always be job assignments that technology cannot replace. There is no substitute for conscientious and dedicated workers.

SHA equipment operators work out of 28 maintenance shops that extend from Snow Hill to Oakland.

 Traffic signal technician working at an intersection.

 MdTA maintenance workers Kelvin Copper (bottom left) and Mark Gordon (bottom right) handle the hard work of maintaining Maryland's toll roads and bridges.

 Each day within SHA's seven district offices, resident maintenance, construction, and traffic staff make routine decisions that may end up saving lives.

 Mechanics at SHA maintenance shops keep equipment ready for the day's work.

Another way to avoid time-consuming intersections is as low tech as the CFI is high tech; it's the roundabout. The roundabout is based on an inviolable rule: the right of way belongs to traffic already in the traffic circle. By its very nature, driving in a circle requires slower speeds, and thus any crashes are less severe, which is why SHA began building them in the 90s.

There's something else about roundabouts. When you landscape the inside of the circle, the roundabout gains style and flare. That's how the humble roundabout found its way from a safety consideration to solidifying its place as one of SHA's current priorities.

The roundabout is the latest arrow in the Context Sensitive Solutions (CSS) quiver aimed at making highways fit in with the ambience of the community. The Towson Roundabout was a model CSS project. The intersection of four major roads at a historic county seat was as complex a set of factors as any highway planner is likely to find. Nevertheless, SHA prepared a traffic roundabout design that not only produced greater efficiency and safety, but added an aesthetic touch with the generous use of landscaping. Most important, fatalities dropped to zero after a spate of seven fatalities that had plagued the intersection in the years immediately preceding the improvements.

Can a commitment to strategies like Smart Growth and Context Sensitive Solutions make more Marylanders want to live in existing towns and suburbs instead of succumbing to the exurb's lure of low density housing on minimally developed land in the country?

Questions like that are why predictions about transportation are such a precarious undertaking. Those types of questions are about who we are and what we value. It's predicting our future.

189

The modern challenge of road construction is to work while maintaining traffic. "We just don't have that much new alignment anymore," says Turk Bradley, a second generation SHA construction inspector. "We have to take care of the roads we have, and that's more of a challenge to me because of the traffic. You have to do something with the traffic."

Hispanic workers often provide the muscle for today's highway construction. Here a group of workers spend a late night and early morning on a new bridge deck.

There are some jobs for which a high-tech solution may never be found.

An SHA maintenance crew from the Office of Maintenance in District 4 poses for a photo after clearing trees downed by Hurricane Isabel, September 18, 2003. Left to right, Walter Calp, Chris Pearce, Carl Randolph, Garry Herman, Mack Brodie, Darius Jackson and Alvin Norris.

If it's reasonable to assume that transportation in the United States will be as different 100 years from now as it was 100 years ago, then it's sobering to consider this: 100 years ago there were only 150 miles of paved highway in the United States and the automobile was a "frail, costly, balky" toy of the rich.

Some futurists say that the Internet highway has the potential to make real highways obsolete. But as long as it's not possible to hug your grandchild or shake hands on a business deal via the Internet, the need for good roads is likely to remain a critical part of who and what we are.

For the last 100 years, Maryland has been a pioneer in traversing great waterways with bridges and tunnels, and building a statewide highway network of expressways and beltway bypasses. If the past is prologue, then we can reasonably assume that Maryland will be at the leading edge of what transportation is like 100 years from now, even if we don't know what that will be.

When some future generation, as distant from us as we are from the ancient Romans, looks at Maryland highways, it will see more than concrete and asphalt, as we see more than stones in Roman roads. A future generation will find clues to grander themes than transportation.

A future generation will find in our farms connected to markets and our cities tied to the world, evidence of an undaunted spirit.

Future generations will find in this place on the Chesapeake Bay, spreading 250 miles from the Atlantic to the Appalachians, evidence of a transformational power that enabled everyday Marylanders to travel as not even the wealthy and privileged could do 100 years before.

This is the legacy of the last 100 years.

Moving forward ...

Neil J. Pedersen
SHA Administrator

After reading the preceding chapters, I have a new appreciation for the significant accomplishments of the hundreds of thousands of individuals who created, maintained and operated the highway system we enjoy today. I hope you do too.

It's remarkable to me how much life in Maryland has changed as a result of the highway network that was built during the last 100 years. As SHA Administrator, part of my job is to predict and plan for Maryland's transportation needs for the future.

Sustaining the system that exists right now appears to be the greatest challenge facing us and future generations. At least for the foreseeable future, personal transport will remain the predominant mode of travel in America. Propulsion systems may be different than those of today; mass transit may offer more choices; and energy availability and cost may exert pressure to make cars smaller and more energy efficient. But cars and trucks are here to stay.

That said, here's a brief look at the factors that may influence the ways we get around in the future.

Safety
Promoting safety has long been a primary mission of the State Highway Administration. So we'll continue to promote safety awareness programs that emphasize the importance of buckling up and on remaining focused on our driving. We'll also continue to work with law enforcement to spot unsafe drivers, and to engineer safety improvements into our roadways.

Vehicle technology improvements also have the potential to vastly improve our safety on the highways. Even now, some leaders in the auto industry have taken on the goal of creating the "accident-proof" car, using systems that detect unsafe conditions and automatically change the speed or direction of the vehicle.

But safety programs and vehicle technology improvements are just the beginning of a march toward the day when injuries and fatalities are a rarity on our highways. It's a day that can't come soon enough for those of us who dedicate outselves to making our highways safe.

Energy
The demand for energy will only get stronger worldwide as the years roll on.

The price and availability of fossil fuels will influence use of the highway system as well as advances in alternative vehicle propulsion systems.

Cars are likely to be smaller and more energy efficient, though not necessarily any less luxurious than consumers expect. And the nation's emphasis on mass transit — and alternatives to the traditional single-occupant auto for commuting to work — will continue to grow.

Environmental Concerns
I'm proud to say that SHA has revolutionized its entire approach to highway project development and environmental protection over the last 25 years, and is now considered a national leader in this area.

For the future, I see much more integrated planning that coordinates transportation with environmental protection and stewardship of environmental resources. Instead of just mitigating environmental impact, we'll seek to improve the environment in every area we touch, including the maintenance of our roadways and facilities.

Operations/Managing Travel Demand
By 2050, the U.S. can expect a population of about 400 million. If we look at current trends, that means we can look forward to approximately 65 million more cars on the road by that time.

SHA is looking at a wide range of tools to mitigate that explosion in demand. That means encouraging drivers to change the time of day they travel; to increase their use of public transit; to charge for the use of less congested lanes; and even encouraging people to telecommute instead of driving to their jobs.

Travelers will have real-time information available on travel conditions and be able to select routes that minimize their travel time. This same information will enable SHA to respond to and clear incidents from the system much faster than we do today.

Technology built into vehicles will also allow for safe travel at closer distances to other vehicles, thus enabling many more vehicles to use existing travel lanes.

Materials Technology

The basic building blocks of the highway system — concrete, asphalt and steel — have vastly improved in durability over the last few decades. The coming years will see a far greater proportion of funds devoted to the reconstruction of existing roads. That means we'll not only be engaged in rebuilding the entire system, but doing so under traffic conditions that will only grow more congested. We will be required to be more innovative in reconstructing roads and bridges much more quickly than we are able to do currently.

Customer Care

The last several decades have seen a radical change in the way highway projects are planned, designed and developed. Maryland has been a leader in this relatively new science of "context sensitive solutions," which turns on its head the way we used to develop projects.

Citizens' expectations for fast, responsive customer service from the State Highway Administration will only continue to grow.

Multiple Modality

With the rise of the global economy and exponential increase in international trade, we're going to see a corresponding increase in the movement of goods. Truck traffic will grow even more rapidly than auto traffic, and efficiency in inter-modal transfers between trucks, ships, airplanes and railcars will become ever more important.

There will also be a much greater emphasis on accommodating the full range of transportation users within our highway rights of way, including transit vehicles, pedestrians and bicycles, as well as the autos and trucks on which we have traditionally focused.

Diversity

The professionals who staff and manage today's SHA represent a far more diverse workforce than ever before, both demographically and in terms of their areas of expertise. Our diversity in gender, race and ethnicity is far more representative of Maryland as a whole, and our participatory management style is far more likely to attract the kind of talent we'll need to offer those who are considering a career in the transportation industry.

That's one of the greatest challenges we'll face as an organization — attracting and retaining professionals who are excited by the idea of service to the public and the opportunity to improve the lives of Maryland's residents and visitors.

For the past 100 years, the challenges that faced our predecessors in the road building industry must have seemed just as daunting. I'm confident though, that simply by building on their legacy of doing the right thing for the citizens of Maryland at every turn, the future of our state's transportation systems will be in good hands.

Acknowledgments

The Maryland Highway Centennial is an opportunity to celebrate the many achievements of those who came before us, those we work with today and those who will carry on and do even greater things in the future. This book and the Maryland Public Television documentary are snapshots in time – when Maryland was transformed in a way no previous 100 years had. Capturing the essence of this period is no easy task and the project took hundreds of people, in big ways and small, to bring it together. The project team borrowed photos, conducted interviews and gathered information far and wide. With a project of this magnitude – events, museum exhibits, a book and documentary, we cannot list everyone who supported or helped to make the Centennial a success. For those not individually listed, please accept our gratitude and know that we appreciate your contributions. Thank you.

Valerie Burnette Edgar, APR, Project Director

Neil J. Pedersen – for believing in the project and understanding that knowing the past helps prepare for the future.

Many thanks to the Centennial Executive Committee, the Maryland Public Television Foundation, the University of Maryland Printing Services and of course our founding and private sponsors.

Special thanks to author Hal Counihan for an enjoyable and readable book, Integrated Designs, Inc. for making it beautiful, Mark Charney for finding thousands of photos and our behind the scenes core team: Sandra F. Dobson, Richard Ervin, Kim Holcomb, Desiree Israel, Mariska Jordan, Mary Keller, Mike Kluh, Gary Monroe, Joe O'Hagan and Cheryl Stambaugh.

Adham Abouassali
Ed Adams
Charles B. Adams
Tim Adcock
Walter J. Addison
Matthew Adeyemi
Allen R. Adon, Jr.
Catherine Agostino
Jennifer Allgair
Muhammad S. Alvi
Dave Ambrose
Charles R. Anderson
Ricardo Anderson
Dorrin L. Armentrout
Ricky Arndt
Linda Ashworth
Dennis R. Atkins
Dave Axline
Sonny Bailey

Tim Baker
Joseph Baldwin
Cindy Bane
Bob Bantz
Shelly Baquol
Rebecca Barber
Joan Barney
Victor Barreira
Art Barrett
Mary F. Barse
Lee Barton
Margot Bartosh
Doug Bast
Tony Battaglia
Michael Baxter
Maxine Beachy Broadwater
Kathy Beard
Roger Beardsley
George R. Beneman, II

Richard Berkow
Jonathan Berle
Raven Berry
Dwayne Bittner
Melissa F. Blair
Jill Blimline
Lynn Block
Terrence "Terry" Blomquist
Gary Boats
Galina Bocharov
James Bolado
Kenton Bontrager
Kellie Boulware
George Bowen
Gretchen Boyd
Mike Boyd
Vanessa Braddy
William Bradley
Karen Branch

Kerry Brandt

Eleanor Bray

Marshaun Brevard

John Brewer

L. A. Brickner

Ken Briggs

Mark Briner

Roger Broadwater

Dale Brock

Carly M. Brooks

Don Brooks

James "Jim" Brown

Marcus Brown

Terry Browning

Anne E. Bruder

Greg Brzozowski

David Buck

Stephen Buckley

Al Budnichuk

John Burch

Philip Burch

Gerald Burgess

Dale Burkins

Edwin T. Burlin

Eileen Burnette

Bruce Burns

Hannah Byron

Jack Cahalan

Dirk Caltrider

M. Slade Caltrider

Norie Calvert

Rudolph C. Cane

Chris Carbone

Cheryl Carley

Clifford T. Carter

Nelson Castellanos

Barry Catterton

Jeanie Cavey

John Paul Cecil

David Chapin

Teresa Charlebois

Dan Cheng

Warren Cherry

Stephen M. Ches

Bill Childs

Vikki Childs

William F. Childs, III

Lisa B. Choplin

Kanwal P. Chopra

Janice Christian

Theodric Clark

Derrick Clemons

Shirlene Cleveland

Ross Clingan

Gene Cofiell

John Coll

Rhonda Collins

Kristen Conner

Betty Conners

James Cook

Greg Cooley

Philip "Pete" C. Cooper

Robert Cooper

George Corbet

Cindy Cordell

Albert Correia

Susan Cortese

Fran Counihan

Ed Countryman

Adrienne Cousler

Caryn Coyle

David Coyne

Eileen Cozart

Anthony Cregger

Bob Cullen

Twanette Culver

J. Joseph Curran, Jr.

Stacy Custer

Gordon Dailey

Edward H. Dalton

Jeff Dalton

K. Mammen Daniel

Mary Davidson

Clayton Davis

John Davis

Jonathan Dean

Claire K. DeBakey

Robert DeBlase

Denny Debus

Mary Deitz

Antonio Delgado

Shalin Desai

Sylvia Desousa

Pat Diamondidis

Michael P. Dignan

Tory DiGregorio

Debra L. Dill

James D. Dilts

Barry Ditto

Alexander Dixon

Vernon N. Dobson

Mike Doherty

Brian Dolan

Leif Dormsjo

Danyelle Dorsey

C. Michael Dougherty

Ronetta Douglas

Robert D. Douglass

Donnie Drewer

Eric Duce

Keith Duerling

Jackson L. Durkee

Rick Dye

Carol A. Ebright

Lou Ege

Fred Eisen

Joshua Eller

Kate Ellis

Wendy Emrich

John Ennis

Joseph Eshleman

Mark Evans

Richard Evans

Tom Evans

Ashley Farmer

Malcomb Faust

Albert L. Feldstein

Susan Filsinger

Natalia Finch

Donald Fisher

Lucretia A. Fisher

Bobby Fisher

Pamela Fitch

Larry Fitzgerald

Mark Flack

Robert L. Flanagan

Pierce Flanigan, III

Frank Flynn

Charlie Fogle
Steve Foster
Theresa Fountain
Bobbi-Jo Fout
Francis B. Francois
Tony Franquelli
Janine Fratantuono
Wayne R. Frazier
Earle S. "Jock" Freedman
Walter Friend, Jr.
Kimberly Frum
Tanja Fulks
John Furman
Russ Furman
Norman Gabriel
Chris Gale
Linda Gale
Judith B. Gan
Kunal Gangopahyay
Cindy Garnand
Steve Gaudio
Robert P. Gay
Willy Gayle
Callie Geller
James Genthner
Dennis German
Bradley Giadiello
Barbara Gibbs Brown
Jonathon Gifford
Cathy Gillen
Robert Gilroy
Eddie Gilyard
Albert B. Gipe
Charlie Gischlar
Shawn Gladden
Malini Glueck
Brian Gneiting
Beverly Goetz
Glenn Goff
Sheila Q. Goodin
Normetha D. Goodrum
Frederick Gottemoeller
Stephen Gradin
Nancy S. Grasmick
Gary Gray
Wayne Gray

Helen Green
Jawauna "Jo" Greene
William Greene
Rick Greenwell
Dave Greenwood
Bruce M. Grey
Marge Gribble
Eric "Smiley" Gross
Patricia Grove
Paul Gudelski
Vicki Guy
Frank T. Haas
Renata Haberkam
Robert Hahan
Mike Haley
Samuel P. Hall
Steven Hall
Sam Halterman
Kathy Hammel
Robert Hammond-Bey
Carl Hampton
Nancy Hampton
Gerry Hanlon
Rick Hansen
Sandy Hansen
Ronnie Hardesty
Timothy J.Hardesty
David Harding
Allison Hardt
William Hardy
Roy Harrell
Carmeletta Harris
Edward Harris
John Harris
Mitchell Harris
Bob Harrison
Joe Harrison
Willard Harvey
Anwer Hasan
Robert Hatcherson
Angela B. Hawkins
Walter Hayes
Robert Healy
Kevin Height
Thomas Heimiller
William K. Hellmann

Carol Helmstetter
Leon Hemsley
Carl Henderson
Erin Henson
Barbara Herron
Ty Hickie
Thomas Hicks
Corey Higdon
Brian Hiles
Marlyn Hill
Marvin Hill
Kelly Hiser
Bill Hobbs
Doris Hoffman
Richard Hoffmann
Almos Holland
Tom Hollowak
Brian Holmes
Liz Homer
Woody Hood
Homer W. Hoover
Fran Horn
Lester Horn
Susan Hose
Randy Houck
Eleanor Huber
George Hudel
Steve Hudson
Chandler Hughes
Phillip Humbertson
David Hunter
Denise Hunter
Dennis Hunter
Sandy Hurley
Debbie Huth
Timothy Hyman
Shep Jackson
Sandra T. Jackson
Martin G. Jacobs
Dorothy Jenkins
Jennifer Jenkins
Sue Jenkins
Dan Johnson
Eric Johnson
James C. Johnson
RaShone Y. Johnson

Ray Johnson

Jim Jones

Madeline Jones

Marvin Jones

Michael J. Jones

Mike Jones

Thomas Jones

Love Joyner

Jack D. Kahl

Robert Kane

Hal Kassoff

Andrew Kaufman

Jennifer Kay

Bob Keeney

Damilola Kehinde

K. C. Keith

Linda Kelbaugh

William J. Kelly

Carol Kendall

Gordon Kennard

Craig F. Kenney

Shameem Khan

Kevin J. Kilgallen

Frederick King

Geneva Kirby

Tom Kirby

Kay Kirk

Glenn Klaverweiden

Jessica Klinefelter

Richard E. Klug

Frank Knapp

Jeff Korman

Andrzej Kosicki

Scott Kozel

Dave Krecz

Kevin Kreis

Leon Kriebel

Pam Kriner

Steve Kuciemba

Linda Kuczinski

Lisa Kwiatkowski

Danny Kyle

Jean Lamana

Leyla Lange

Darryl "Bear" Laney

Christina Lavoie

Alex Lee

Paris Lee

William K. Lee, III

Michael Leicht

George "Butch" Lerring

Andrew Levine

Brenda Lewis

Frank Lewis

Mike Lewis

Richard Lindsay

Marc Lipnick

Ron Lipps

Howard Lloyd

David W. Logan

Brian Long

Deborah Lotchte

Amber Lovejoy

David Lowdermilk

Butch Lundgren

Roberta Lyles

Joseph A. Madison

Daniel J. Maletic

Dave Malkowski

Steve Manis

Randy Mardres

Robert Markline

David Marks

Alvin Marquess

K.R. Marshall

Michael Marsolais

Dave Martin

Robert Mashewske

Darlene Mason

Vanessa Mason

Paul Matys

Terry Maxwell

Jeff McBride

Carol McCabe

Deidre McCabe

Geoffrey McCammon

Kirk McClelland

Robert McClure

Marion J.McCoy

Sheryl McCreary

Harry McCullough

Billy McGinty

John McGrain

Fred McGuigan

Tanya M. McIntosh

Joann McIntyre

Thaïs Meadows

Raleigh D. Medley

Michael J. Meek

Laura Mehiel

Kelly Melhem

Susan Meoni

Bruce Mercer

Linda Merriken

Ken Merrill

Brian Messing

Louis D. Metz

Charles Meyer

Diane Michael

Kimberly Michalov

Susan Middaugh

Bobbi Jean Mihailovich

Joseph M. Miklochik

Bob Miller

Joe Miller

Joseph R. Miller

Nicole Miller

Sam Miller

Samuel R. Miller, Jr.

Bart Mitchell

David Mitchell

Wesley Mitchell

Darrell Mobley

Peter Moe

Wallace Montgomery

Grover Moore

Lorraine Moore

Nate Moore

Sam Moore

Raymond Moravec

Jay Morgan

Scot Morrell

Alvin Morris

Teri Moss

Linda Mott

Heather Murphy

Steve Murphy

Patricia Murray

Robert Murry

Brad Myers

Ed Myers

Derrell Neal

Wayne Neely

Terry Neimeyer

Bruce Nelson

Tracy Newman

Michael Newton

Todd Nichols

Jerald Nolan

John Nolan

Tim Norman

James Ober

Kathy Ochrzcin

Okey "Innocent" Odinammadu

James J. O'Donnell

Calvin Ogletree

Johnny Oliver

Robert Olsen

Joel Oppenheimer

Natasha OrtizFortier

Jim Otradovec

Andy Owen

Jane Page

George Papaspyrou

Edward Papenfuse

William R. Park

Bobby Parker

Charles T. Parker

Charlie Parker, III

Martin B. Parker

Robin Parker Cox

Richard Parsons

Joe Pascuzzi

Atul Patel

Monica Pats

Greg Patterson

Marshal Paul

Steve Pearce

James Peck

Melinda Peters

Harry Phillips

Peter P. Phillips

Veronica Piskor

Dawnetta Plumer

Ken Polcak

Matt Pollack

Kim Polyniak

Mary Poore

William W. Porter

Frank W. Prochazka

Sidney Proctor

Catie Proulx

Bob Prouse

Mike Pruett

John Pszeniczny

Cindi Ptak

Cathy Pugh

Tim Pugh

Karuna Pujara

Clyde E. Pyers

Sabrina Quirate

Curtis A. Racavich

Curtis Racavich, III

Robert Rager

Lora Rakowski

Cheri Randow

Johnathan Ray

Hassan Raza

Justin Readmond

Lindsay Reilly

Scott Reynolds

Debbie Rice

Lou Robbins

Sephone Roberts

Jacquie Robinson

Edward Rodenhizer

Debbie Rodgers

Dennis Rodgers

Nolan Rogers

Samantha Rollins

Brian Romanowski

Dave Rosage

Douglas Rose

David Rosen

Patricia Ross

Shannon Rousey

Gil Rushton

Karen Saab

Ziad A. Sabra

Bernie Saggese

Jeanne Samuels

Paul Samuels

Dan Sanayi

Dennis Sanders

Steve Sandkuhler

Sheri Sanford

Sonal Sanghavi

Badri N. Satwah

Joseph Savoy

John Scally

Julie M. Schablitsky

John Schene

Richard Scher

Richard Schindel

Ronald Schlundt

Robert W. Schoeberlein

Cheryl Schreiber

Robert K. Scrivener

LaVerna Scruggs

Bruce E. Seely

Bridgid Seering

Gayle Seward

Don Sewell

Stephanie Shafer

Greg Shafer

Rick Shagogue

Romi Shah

Gary L. Shank

Mike Sheets

Don Sherin

Sylvia Sherman

Robert Shindle

Monty Shoemaker

Marty Shorter

Zvi Shoubin

Robert J. Shuman

William Shure

Victor Siaurusaitis

Jill Sibley

Vicki Silva

Doug Simmons

Robert Simon

Cynthia D. Simpson

Dennis Simpson

Anthony Sinclair

Nancy Sites

Steve Sites

John Skidmore

Matt Skocik

Gregory I. Slater

Marty Slater

Timothy Smidt

Angela Smith

Donna Smith

Duane Smith

Jeff Smith

Kurt Smith

Tim Smith

William Ron Smith

David Snead

Barbara Snyder

Jesse Snyder

Barbara Solberg

Romaine Somerville

T.J. Spampinato

Donald H. Sparklin

Tom Sparkman

Cheryl Sparks

James R. Spear

Emily Oland Squires

Tim Stambaugh

James "Jim" Stambaugh

Jim Star

Joan Stark

Lee Starkloff

Wayne Steinhouse

Tom Stevens

Linda Stevens

James Stimpert

Paul Stout

Eileen K. Straughan

Edgar Stubbs

Beverley Swaim-Staley

Jim Swauger

Eric Tabacek

Terri Tabesh

Al Tate

Andrew Tate

Damonnen Taylor

Monica Taylor-Clowney

Katie Teague

Linda Thomas

James R. Thomas, Jr.

Dave Thomey

W.C. Thompson

Doc Tisdale

Eric Tombs

Nick Torres

Les Townsend

Walter Townsend

Jo Ann Tracey

Kimberly M. Tran

Philip Troll

Joel Trotta

Ann Turkos

Gail Tutko

LeRoy Tyree

Dan Uebersax

Larry D.Unger

Paul Upton

Tabetha Vanlandingham

Carol Vassallo

Glenn C. Vaughan

Harry Vaughn

Keith Vaughn

Raja Veeramachaneni

Alex Vitalo

Carl Vogel

Richard Wagman

Fred Wagner

Stanley Wake

Rey Walker

John W. Wallace

Kenlin "Vic" Walton

Fran Ward

Henry Ward

Mary Lou Ward

Thomas Ward

Dick Wardenfelt

John Warnick

George Wathen

Carl Watkins

Rudie Weeks, II

Richard Weingroff

Bill Weishaar

John Weisner

Greg Welker

Jill Welsh

Harry Wetklow

Ray Wetzel

James J. White

Steve Whitecotton

Patty Whitfield

Cheron Wicker

Randall R.Wiley

Jack Williams

Jennifer Williams

Jessica Williams

Joyce Williams

Parker F. Williams

Robert Williams

Jeffery Willis

Kevin Wilson

Chisa Winstead

John Wiser

Jerome B. Wolff

Donald Wolkoff

Jim Wompler

Richard Woo

George Wood

Howard Wood

Valerie Woodson-Pini

Roland Woodward

Tami Worthington

Richard Wray

Jim Wright

John Wright

Terry Wright

William Wright

Jim Yarsky

Kim Yates

Winston Van Yerrell

Dennis Yoder

Buel Young

Garfield Young

Tessa Young

Russell Yurek

Rich Zeller

Carole Zentz

Mike Zezeski

Matthew Zulkowski

Photo Credits

COVER

Spreading rock for macadam road. P. Flanigan and Sons

INTRODUCTORY PAGES

Johnstown Good Roads Committee. William "Scoops" Claude
  Collection c/o Maryland Archives

National Pike, Keyser's Ridge. Leo J. Beachy photo c/o Maxine
  Broadwater

Roadway with Black-eyed Susans. SHA Collections

District 6 snow plow 1920s. District 6 SHA Collections

Snow plow 1990s. SHA Collections

Woodrow Wilson Bridge. Historic American Building Survey

Woodrow Wilson Bridge. Roger Miller photo copyright 2007
  c/o Johnson, Mirmiran & Thompson

DEDICATION

Fallsway. Enoch Pratt Free Library

Governor Martin O'Malley. Maryland State Government

MDOT Transportation Secretary John D. Porcari. Maryland
  State Government

EXECUTIVE COMMITTEE

Patrick Flanigan and work crew. P. Flanigan and Sons

Executive Committee photos. Maryland State Government

TITLE PAGE

Asphalt paving crew. Hughes Co. photo c/o Enoch Pratt Free
  Library

TABLE OF CONTENTS

Page 1

Cars in traffic, 1920s. SHA Collections

INTRODUCTION

Page 2

Tobacco road roller, Harpers Weekly, 1859. Maryland
  Historical Society

Maryland map. SHA Collections

Page 3

Fairview Inn. Enoch Pratt Free Library

CHAPTER 1

Page 4

Conestoga Wagon, from Fair of the Iron Horse, B&O Railroad
  Centennial Celebration, 1929. Baltimore & Ohio Railroad
  c/o Enoch Pratt Free Library

Conestoga Wagon, "Going to the Gunpowder Quarterly
  Meeting," 1859. Enoch Pratt Free Library

Page 5

General Braddock, John Kennedy Lacock. SHA Collections

Page 6

"The First American Macadam Road." Carl Rakeman painting
  c/o Federal Highway Administration

Macadam mallet. Mark Charney photo c/o Douglas Bast,
  Boonsboro Museum

Rebuilding the National Road. William "Scoops" Claude
  Collection c/o Maryland Archives

Page 7

Frederick Road Turnpike House. Identified by William
  Hollifield c/o Enoch Pratt Free Library

Baltimore--Reisterstown Turnpike stock. Baltimore Co. Legacy
  project

Baltimore--Yorktown Turnpike stock. Baltimore Co. Legacy
  project

Horse drawn grubbing. District 1 SHA Collections

Page 8

Lawrence "Speedy" Bittinger. Leo J. Beachy photo c/o Maxine
  Broadwater

Page 9

National Pike Keyser's Ridge. Leo J. Beachy photo c/o Maxine
  Broadwater

Page 10

Johnstown Good Roads Committee. William "Scoops" Claude
  Collection c/o Maryland Archives

Baltimore Co. Good Roads Truck. William "Scoops" Claude
  Collection c/o Maryland Archives

Page 11

Samuel M. Shoemaker II. Enoch Pratt Free Library

Hagerstown bicycle rally. Enoch Pratt Free Library

Charles S. Diggs. Louis Diggs family photo c/o Baltimore Co.
  Legacy project

Farmer with ox. Enoch Pratt Free Library

A Lasting Legacy

Today's highways are a testament to the contributions of engineers and contractors from private industry in alliance with the leadership and dedication of those in public service. The Maryland Highway Centennial marks 100 years of modern road building and maintenance, and an opportunity to raise awareness of how highways support Maryland's economy and quality of life. More importantly, the Centennial is a platform for highway professionals to promote traffic safety, our paramount and universal goal.

The Centennial Project is a partnership between the Maryland Quality Initiative, the Federal Highway Administration, the Maryland Department of Transportation, State Highway Administration and Transportation Authority, as well as Maryland Public Television. The effort includes this book, a Maryland Public Television documentary, displays at the Baltimore Museum of Industry, Maryland Science Center and Baltimore Washington International Thurgood Marshall Airport, a website and a wide variety of community outreach events.

The project is primarily funded by a federal grant and matching funds raised by private industry. In the course of raising funds for the effort, visionary leaders in private industry looked beyond this commemorative occasion and set about creating a lasting legacy that would serve future generations. Considering the more than 600 fatalities annually from traffic crashes in Maryland at the time of printing of this book, they established the Maryland Highway Safety Foundation, a private 501(c)3 corporation. The mission of the organization is to promote highway safety and driver education, and offer support in many ways to emergency response providers long after this centennial celebration has concluded.

We are grateful to the longtime leaders in the transportation industry who spearheaded this effort. The new foundation joined as a partner in the Centennial Project and provides a

unique opportunity for business leaders to make a difference in traffic safety. The website is www.mdhighwaysafety.org.

Maryland Highway Safety Foundation
Founded 2008

We also gratefully acknowledge the contributions of the sponsors on the following pages who helped to make this project possible, and whose contributions will help to promote safety for all Marylanders for years down the road.

As this book went to press, one of the founders of the Maryland Highway Safety Foundation suddenly passed away. We fondly remember Pierce Flanigan III and thank him for his visionary leadership.

our e-mission

At General Motors, our environmental mission is simple: take America from gas-friendly to gas-free. It's a journey that's already begun. Right now, we offer the most models that get an EPA-estimated 30 mpg or better on the highway. We also have 3 million FlexFuel vehicles on the road today capable of running on E85 ethanol, which burns cleaner than gasoline.

We're offering eight hybrid cars, trucks and SUVs in the 2008 calendar year, including the industry's first two-mode hybrid that increases both city and highway mileage.*

And we're not stopping there. Our concept Chevy Volt extended-range electric vehicle — designed to give nearly 80% of Americans a gas-free commute — is creating a buzz as it gets closer.** And right now, in places like Southern California, New York and Washington, D.C., the world's largest test market fleet of hydrogen vehicles is on the streets.† At GM, we believe there is more than one way to get to the future. Our goal is to be the car company that takes you there.

gm.com

CHEVROLET • BUICK • PONTIAC • GMC • SATURN • HUMMER • SAAB • CADILLAC

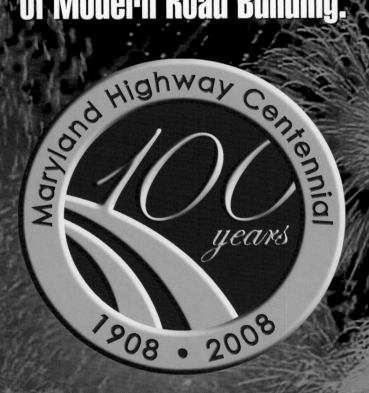

213

Maryland's Highway Centennial

John E. Greiner

1908

Congratulations on a Century of Progress in Modern Road Building

2008

URS
Engineers Architects Planners

Also Celebrating 100 Years in Maryland

215

We remember when you were only this tall...

K C I
TECHNOLOGIES

A Proud Sponsor of the Maryland Centennial

KCI Technologies Inc. has its origins in a small engineering firm that began operating out of a Baltimore County basement in 1955. From these humble beginnings sprang one of the largest employee-owned companies headquartered in Maryland. Today, our roughly 1,000 employee owners operate throughout the Northeast, Southeast and Mid-Atlantic.

KCI offers a full range of multi-disciplined services for transportation projects, including highway, structural, traffic planning and engineering, as well as surveying, construction management and inspection. We also offer water and natural resources management services, GIS development, hazardous waste remediation, utilities coordination, public involvement, and geotechnical and subsurface utility engineering.

With revenues of more than $142 million in 2007, *Engineering News-Record* magazine has consistently placed KCI among the top consulting engineering firms in the country. We are proud to have played a part in developing Maryland's comprehensive transportation network and are honored to celebrate its highway centennial.

Employee-owned Since 1988 | www.kci.com

MD I-195

MD I-270 Y-Split

MD 210 Interchange

It's been one fantastic ride.
Congratulations on a century of awe-inspiring progress.

PB
100
YEARS ®

© 2008 Parsons Brinckerhoff.

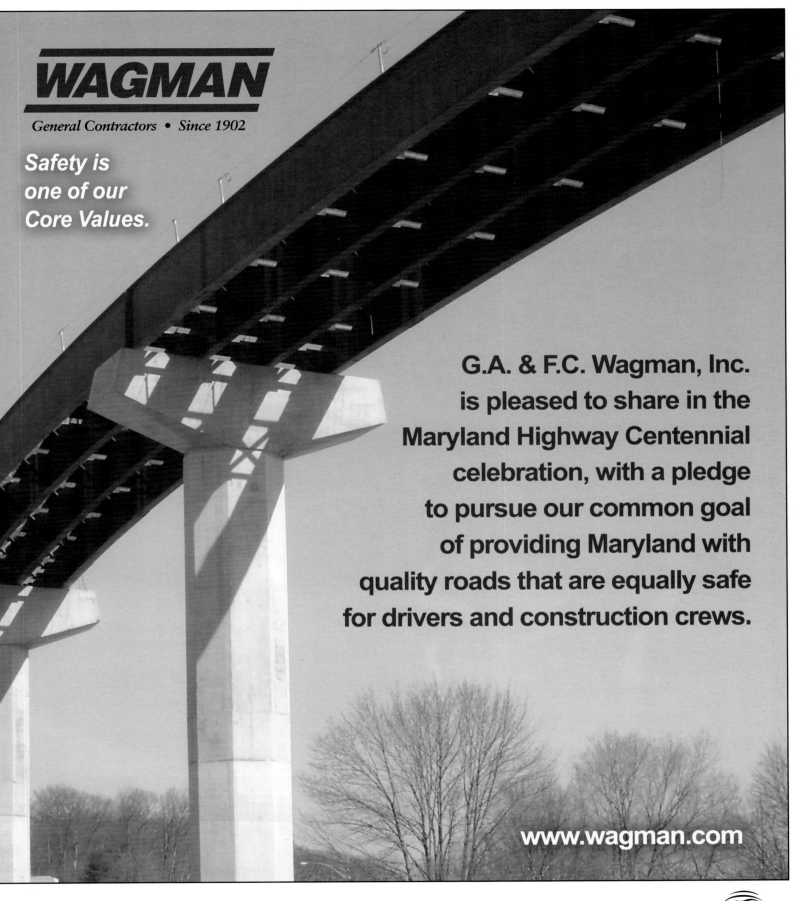

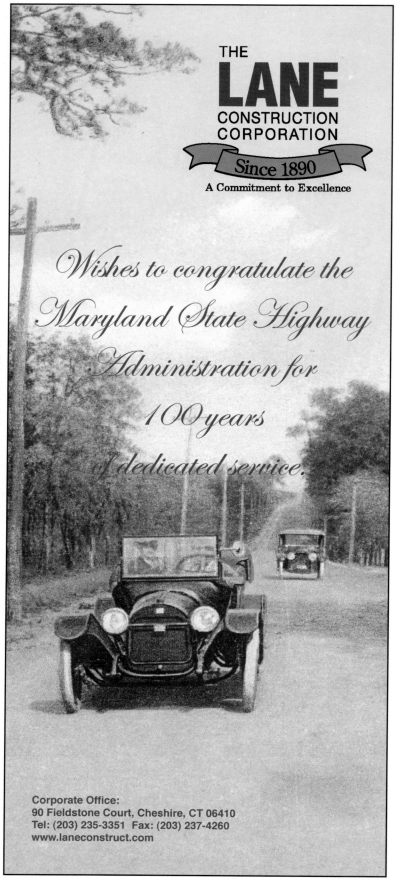

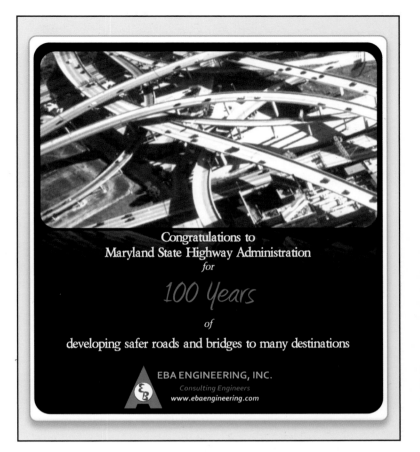

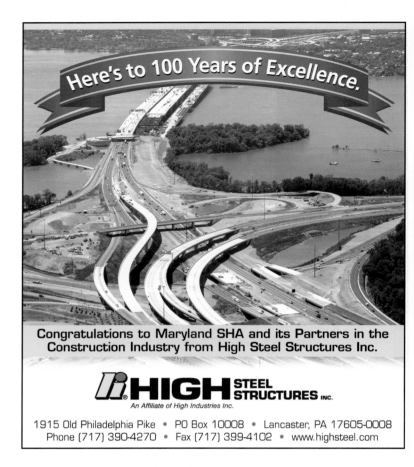
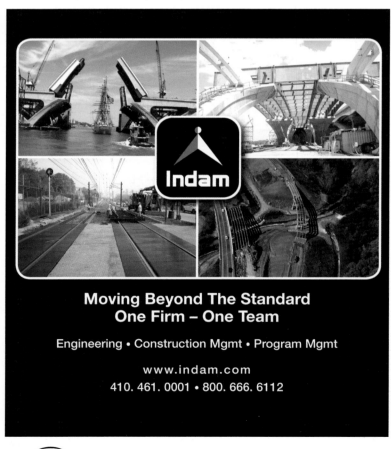

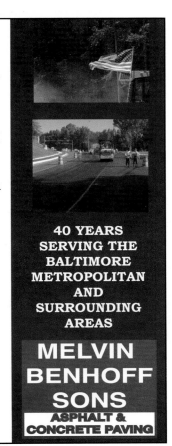

Thank you to our sponsors.

PLATINUM SPONSORS

GMPT Baltimore Transmission
Johnson, Mirmiran & Thompson
Rummel, Klepper & Kahl
URS

GOLD SPONSORS

Ford Motor Driving Skills for Life
HNTB Corporation
KCI Technologies
PB
Wagman
Whitman, Requardt & Associates

SILVER SPONSORS

Corman Construction Inc.
David A. Bramble
E. Stewart Mitchell
E2CR
HMS Insurance Associates
Kelly & Associates
The Lane Construction Corporation
National Capital Industries
P. Flanigan & Sons
Wallace Montgomery & Associates
Whitney Bailey Cox & Magnani
Wilbur Smith Associates

BRONZE SPONSORS

Chaney Enterprises
EBA Engineering
Fox Industries
Greenman-Pedersen, Inc.
High Steel Structures
Indam Engineers
McCormick Taylor
Melvin Benhoff Sons, Inc.
Priceless Industries
Reliable Contracting
Standard Equipment

FRIEND SPONSORS

Aggregate Industries, Mid-Atlantic
Constellation Design Group
Gray & Son, Inc.
Maryland Paving, Inc.
Midasco
Paul J. Rach, Inc.
Smith-Midland
Traffic Group
Villa Julie College
Wilson T. Ballard Company

PATRON SPONSORS

A. Morton Thomas & Associates
AAA Mid-Atlantic
ADDCO
American Traffic Safety Services
Aris Melissaratos
Bone Safety Signs
Century Engineering
Cianbro
Concrete General
Development Facilitators
Dewberry
DMJM Harris
Edward & Lorraine Moran/CNA Surety
Highway Safety Services
JJID Inc.
Marinis Bros.
Mid Atlantic Machinery
Nolan Associates
Pennoni Associates
Plastic Safety Systems, Inc.
Quixote
Schnabel Engineering
Sidhu Associates
Slurry Pavers, Inc.
STV
Vulcan Materials Company
W. R. Meadows of PA

BOOSTER SPONSORS

American Highway Users Alliance
American Road and Transport Builders
    Assoc.
Bhavana & Neeraj Singh
Brudis & Associates
GeoStructures
Maryland Motor Trucking Association
PENN Line Service
Prime Engineering
RJM Engineering
Saul Ewing, LLP
United Parcel Service

SUPPORTER SPONSORS

American Society of Highway Engineers
BST Advisory Network
Guardrails Etc.
Hunt Valley Contractors
Maryland Highway Users Federation
NuStar
Ramar Moving Systems, Inc.
Sabra Wang Associates
WMDA
Woman's Transportation Seminar

Index